ELEMENTS OF

Chemical
Thermodynamics

This book is in the

ADDISON-WESLEY SERIES

IN THE PRINCIPLES OF CHEMISTRY

———————————————

FRANCIS T. BONNER

Consulting Editor

ELEMENTS OF

Chemical Thermodynamics

LEONARD K. NASH

Department of Chemistry
Harvard University

ADDISON-WESLEY PUBLISHING COMPANY, INC.

Reading, Massachusetts · Palo Alto · London

Preface

Another book on classical thermodynamics: what can it offer that is new? In this of all subjects anything true has certainly been said before, and anything not before so said is probably wrong. What novelty I dare claim is then more a matter of omissions than of inclusions; still more a matter of presentation than of content.

I have sought to display the physical content of thermodynamics as distinct from mathematical manipulations that, for the beginning student, function less often as the powerful tools they are intended to be than as an opaque screen drawn between him and the physical concepts he must grasp. I have used only a dozen of the most elementary operations of the calculus—all of which are explained in Appendix I. In several thermodynamic developments sophisticated elegance must then give way to a simple clumsiness, and certain other developments cannot even be attempted. However, these losses are, in my view, wholly outweighed by the possibility of that gain I have pursued to the exclusion of all others: the focus of attention is everlastingly maintained on the physical concepts involved. In some sense corollary to this primary intent is the effort made to indicate the physical correlates of the entropy concept. While stressing repeatedly that we transact the business of classical thermodynamics in complete independence of all hypotheses about the nature of matter, energy, and entropy, I have nevertheless seized every opportunity to give rough statistical *interpretations* of what it is we obtain from entropy *calculations*.

That aspect of thermodynamics I believe to be at once most striking and most important to the beginning student is the possibility of calculating, from thermal data, the equilibrium constant of a chemical reaction not before measured, perhaps not even achieved. The entire train of argument has been shaped to bring this calculation within reach by displaying the thermodynamic roots of the whole concept of equilibrium. Indeed, I have treated no topic that I regard as far from the highroad towards the concept of equilibrium; and, further, none for which partial differentiation seems absolutely required. A word about what this book *doesn't* do may then be in order. The omissions I most regret (easily made good by any teacher having time and the resolve to do so) are the following:

1. The concept of chemical potential seems to demand a development setting out from a reconstruction of the first principle applicable to open systems, and making extensive use of partial differential formulations.

2. The phase rule—pretty and powerful, "exact but qualitative" in the words of Lewis and Randall (1st and 2nd editions)—falls far from the focus of a treatment of thermodynamics that has "the primary purpose of making it readily applicable to quantitative and numerical calculations."

3. Experimental calorimetry—the backbone of thermodynamics—I handle in lecture demonstration and laboratory exercise, and I have not made the (probably vain) attempt to give an equivalent presentation in print.

This book assumes no more than a sound background in high-school mathematics and physics and familiarity with the leading quantitative concepts of the traditional introductory college chemistry course. Though some of the problems (grouped together in Appendix II) are reasonably searching, none requires calculus for its solution. Certainly this first introduction to thermodynamics cannot stand in lieu of a more advanced treatment of the same subject, but it should permit that advanced course to go faster and further, while at the same time providing more challenging intellectual fare for the beginning student. Thus, for example, a fully mathematized axiomatic treatment of thermodynamics in the style of Gibbs is a rewarding intellectual experience for the advanced student, while to grasp for the first time the *full* significance of the simple Carnot cycle is also a thoroughly rewarding intellectual experience readily accessible to the beginner.

A set of notes prepared by B. H. Mahan, and made available to me through his courtesy, first taught me that, and *how*, by a skillful choice of methods one can convey the substance of thermodynamics even to beginning students. The design of my own presentation owes much to his pioneering effort. I have drawn several important arguments from *The Structure of Physical Chemistry*, by C. N. Hinshelwood, and to E. F. Caldin's *An Introduction to Chemical Thermodynamics* (Oxford: University Press 1958) I am heavily indebted for several entire chains of reasoning leading up to key points. I acknowledge with thanks permission to reproduce from this same book two quotations of text (on pp. 57 and 71) and the two tables I have numbered 4 and 5. Other publishers have kindly consented to the reproduction in the present work of the following items: the figure I have numbered 26 is redrawn from Hildebrand and Scott's *Solubility of Non-Electrolytes* (New York: Reinhold 1950); Figure 28 and Table 2 are taken from the indicated pages of the Journal of the American Chemical Society; the thermochemical data tabulated in Appendix III are reproduced from *Selected Values of Chemical Thermodynamic Properties*, ed. F. D. Rossini *et al.*, published as National Bureau of Standards Circular 500; the quoted paragraph on p. 61 is reproduced from Lewis, Randall, Pitzer, and Brewer's *Thermodynamics*, 2nd ed. (New York: McGraw-Hill 1961); the quoted passage on p. 89 is reproduced from J. E. Coates' Haber Memorial Lecture, in vol. IV of the Chemical Society Memorial Lectures; and the quoted passage on p. 90 is reproduced from an article by Ernest Nagel in *Daedalus*, Winter 1959 (reprinted in *Education in the Age of Science;* New York: Basic Books 1959).

I am profoundly grateful for many valuable suggestions made to me by R. S. Berry, S. Golden, W. E. Klemperer, and P. J. Urnes, and by the editor of this series, F. T. Bonner. The students of Chemistry 2 in the academic year 1961–62 struggled valiantly with a preliminary version of this material. Many of them have helped me by pointing out specific obscurities and errors; and I learned much from the successes and failures of the class as a whole. I am indebted to R. H. Holm, who read the proof of the preliminary version; to M. K. Wilson and J. E. Cohen, who read the galleys of the present version; and to H. S. Kahn and M. Z. Lewin, who worked through all the problems and suggested several corrections and many improvements. I am arrogant enough to suppose that—despite the best efforts of all who have been kind enough to assist me—I have, completely unaided, managed to maintain a steady-state concentration of obscurities and errors. I take this opportunity to thank those who will, in future, make these failures known to me.

April 1962   L. K. N.

Contents

Introduction

Thermodynamics rests squarely on an experimental foundation immense both in breadth and depth, but—like the similarly founded disciplines of classical, relativistic, and quantum mechanics—thermodynamics is constructed in the form of a postulational system that may seem to hang from premises floating in a sphere of higher abstractions. From three such premises, however, we can and do deduce—and so explain or rationalize—an immense array of widely (and often apparently universally) applicable relations previously known only as empirical laws, as well as many others previously not even so known. The marvelous generality here displayed by thermodynamics is entirely attributable to the abstractness of its premises. Generated by a creative abstraction from the manifold details and particularities of individual experiences, the premises of thermodynamics are stripped insofar as possible of everything referring to specific events—and so become at least potentially available for the construal of events of the most diverse varieties. Classical thermodynamics, a discipline of immense generality, is also one of immense reliability. "Certainly," says Gibbs, "one is building on an insecure foundation, who rests his work on hypotheses concerning the constitution of matter." Turning on an absolutely minimal array of postulates and auxiliary assumptions— cunningly contriving to treat of matter while making no assumptions whatever about the constitution (atomic or otherwise) of matter—classical thermodynamics furnishes predictions having an almost unrivalled degree of certainty.

Classical thermodynamics displays a characteristic union of generality and reliability, but it is also a discipline having certain limitations no less characteristic. Thermodynamics treats of *systems*—parts of the world that definite boundaries isolate conceptually (and often, with a good degree of approximation, experimentally) from the rest of the world. The *state* of such a system is thermodynamically defined by specifying the values of a set of measurable parameters sufficient that each of the remaining variables can have but one value—so that one is assured of an accurate reproduction of the system whenever specified values of the defining parameters obtain. The parameters most used by chemists are pressure, volume, temperature, and composition (expressed in partial pressures, mole fractions, or the like). Of these the temperature—and, to a considerable extent, the pressure—

1

does not have a well-defined value save for a statistically large system. That is, given the (Maxwellian) distribution of molecular velocities, a single molecule, or even a small group of molecules, does not have a definable temperature. Thermodynamics is then characteristically a science of *macroscopic* systems that have determinate values of such parameters as p and T—and this restriction seems absolutely enforced by the limited (i.e., statistical) validity of the second principle of thermodynamics.

Classical thermodynamics is concerned with the *equilibrium states* of systems, NOT with the *paths* by which different states may be connected; and NOT with the *rates* at which the paths may be traversed and the states attained. Thermodynamics is then, if you please, rather more the science of the possible in principle than the science of the attainable in practice. What thermodynamics finds impossible we cannot hope to achieve, and we are spared the investment of effort in a vain endeavor; but to achieve in practice what thermodynamics finds possible in principle may still require an immense endeavor. For example, thermodynamic calculations show that diamond should be formed from graphite at temperatures of 1000–3000°K under pressures of 30,000 to 100,000 atmospheres. Attempts to achieve this conversion, however, were for long totally unsuccessful. Having confidence in thermodynamics, one attributes these failures to slowness of the reaction, and one perseveres in the endeavor to achieve in practice what thermodynamics indicates as possible in principle. With the construction of equipment competent to maintain the required conditions for hours, rather than seconds—and with the discovery of an effective catalyst—the synthesis of diamond was finally achieved in 1954.

Heat and Work. In much the same period that the equivalence of heat and work was first established, the limited efficiency of steam engines posed a problem from which the science of thermodynamics developed. Even today introductory expositions of thermodynamics take their departure from the familiar concepts of work and heat—though the concept of work is far from uncomplicated, and today it is only metaphorically that we conceive heat in the original ("thermo-dynamic") sense of a "something," i.e. "caloric," that "flows."

Heat is distinguished from other forms of energy by a unique asymmetry that finds quantitative expression in the second principle of thermodynamics. Other forms of energy seem in principle to be 100% interconvertible, and all are 100% convertible into heat. But heat itself is *not* 100% convertible to *any* other form of energy: e.g., no heat engine ever does (or, we think, can) convert into work all the heat supplied to it. Quantities of heat (and thence of other forms of energy converted into and measured "calorimetrically" as heat) are expressed in joules or calories, ~ 4.2 joules being equivalent to 1 calorie.

Work we will regard as energy lost from a system by mechanisms other than radiation and thermal conduction. Of the great many species of work of which thermodynamics renders account we consider but two:

Electrical work = Potential difference · Charge transported
(in joules)   (in volts)   (in coulombs)

Mechanical work = Force · Distance in direction of force
(in joules)   (in   (in meters)
                    newtons)

Actually we will confine ourselves to one special type of mechanical work —that due to changes of volume in the presence of a finite pressure. Consider the work done when, as shown in Fig. 1, a piston is thrust a distance l into a cylinder of cross section A. If, by definition,

$$w = F \cdot l,$$

then we can also write

$$w = \frac{F}{A} \cdot A \cdot l.$$

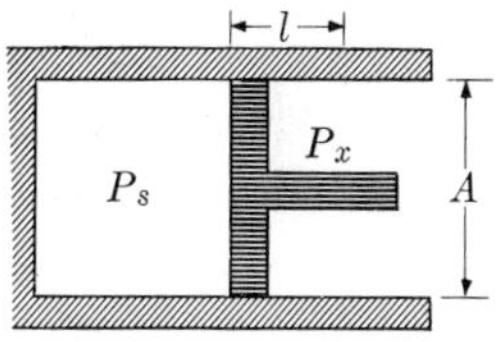

FIGURE 1

But then the quotient F/A is a pressure, p; and $A \cdot l$ is the area subject to that pressure times the distance through which the pressure acts— which product corresponds to the change of volume, ΔV. Thus

$$w = p\,\Delta V.$$

If pressure is expressed in atmospheres and volume change in liters, work will be expressed in units of liter-atmospheres, where one liter-atmosphere represents ~ 100 joules.

The situation is perhaps clearest if we consider a piston-cylinder system, but the same equation applies generally. Consider that we represent our system on a plot of pressure against volume. Then if the pressure remains constant throughout the volume change, as in Fig. 2(a), the work is represented by the shaded *area* under the plot of pressure, and is easily obtained as the product $p\,\Delta V$. If the pressure changes, however—as in plots (b)

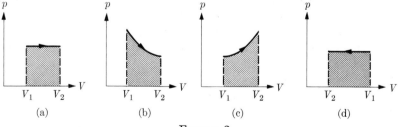

(a)   (b)   (c)   (d)

FIGURE 2

and (c)—then we must multiply each infinitesimal change of volume dV by the pressure corresponding to it. The sum of all these infinitesimals is again the area under the pressure plot. If p can be expressed as $f(V)$ then, as shown in Appendix I, this area is at once obtainable by application of the integral calculus:

$$w = \int_{V_1}^{V_2} p \, dV.$$

To what pressure does p correspond? Imagine a massless piston driven back frictionlessly against an external pressure $P_x = 0$. However large the internal pressure P_s, and however great the *opportunity* to do work that is dissipated, in this case (corresponding to the expansion of an ideal gas into a vacuum) *no work is performed*. To determine the work done between one equilibrium state and another we must take $p = P_x$: *the $P \, \Delta V$ work done by a system is a function of the external, NOT of the internal, pressure.* Often as chemists we face problems that can be solved only by relating the work term to the internal pressure of the system, and it is possible to conceive one particular condition in which the work term can, in principle, be expressed in terms of the internal pressure. We imagine a hypothetical state of affairs in which at all times the external pressure differs only infinitesimally from the internal pressure. We imagine an ideal piston that, under the impulsion of this pressure difference, moves perfectly frictionlessly at an infinitesimal velocity compatible with the suppression of all other dissipative losses of the capacity to do work. Taking dP as the infinitesimal pressure difference, we then write $P_x = P_s \pm dP$, so that

$$\text{Work} = \int_{V_1}^{V_2} P_x \, dV = \int_{V_1}^{V_2} (P_s \pm dP) \, dV = \int_{V_1}^{V_2} (P_s \, dV \pm dP \, dV).$$

The term $dP \, dV$ is an infinitesimal of higher order and can be neglected; so that the work (w_{rev}) done under these special ("reversible") conditions —and *only* under these conditions—can be expressed as

$$w_{\text{rev}} = \int_{V_1}^{V_2} P_s \, dV = P_s(V_2 - V_1) = P_s \, \Delta V. \qquad (1)$$

$\llcorner$ IF the pressure is constant

Given the stipulated conditions, the work done during the expansion of the gas differs only infinitesimally from the work required to recompress it to its original condition—whence the designation "reversible."

Observe that *always*, when computing a Δ term, we subtract the initial value of the parameter from the final value. The work term will then be positive when $V_2 > V_1$, and negative when $V_2 < V_1$. That is, w is positive when work is done *by* the system, *expanding against* an external pressure, and w is negative when work is done *on* the system, *compressed by* an external pressure. Thus in Fig. 2(a) the work term is positive, while in Fig. 2(d) it is negative. Given an interest in steam engines, this assignment of signs was perfectly natural: the output is the work done *by* the engine, and any work required to be done *on* the engine is a negative term, diminishing the *net* output of work. The signs given to heat terms (q) are referable to the same original interest in engines. Thus q is positive for transfers of heat *to* the system, negative for transfers of heat *from* the system. The latter is a heat *loss*, diminishing the net efficiency of the engine.

The First Principle of Thermodynamics

Thermodynamics treats of states produced by exchanges of heat and work between a system and its surroundings. But the quantities of heat and work involved are, we will find, *not* uniquely fixed by the initial and final states of a system. In practice we find it expedient to devise concepts that are functions of state alone, and thus independent of the paths taken between states and, more generally, of the history of the system. The first of five such concepts we shall use is *energy;* and the first principle of thermodynamics asserts the conservation, or constancy, of energy.

Consider a volume of water stationary in a pool at the head of a waterfall. It has what we may call "privilege of position," in that once it has dropped over the fall we must do work to return it to its original position. As the water passes over the fall its "privilege of position" vanishes, but at the same time it acquires *"vis viva,"* the "living force" of motion. By passing the water through a turbodynamo, we strip it of its *vis viva* and simultaneously acquire electric power—which vanishes in favor of heat if the dynamo is shorted through a resistance. If the water drops directly to the bottom of the fall, without passing through the turbine, *vis viva* disappears without the production of electric power—but in that case heat is produced directly (i.e., water at the bottom of the fall has a temperature slightly higher than that with which it left the top of the fall). Now *a priori* there is *no* reason to suppose that "privilege of position," *"vis viva,"* electric power, and heat—qualitatively apparently utterly different—stand in any relation whatever to each other. Experience, however, teaches us to regard them all simply as diverse manifestations of a single fundamental potency: energy (Gr. *energos*, active; from *en*, in + *ergon*, work). That is, experience teaches us that the disappearance of one "species of energy" is always accompanied by the appearance of another such species—e.g., as above mechanical potential energy gives way to kinetic energy which gives way to electric energy which gives way to heat. Far more than this, experience teaches us that the interconversions of species of energy take place in accordance with invariant ratios. That is, when mechanical energy disappears, an "equivalent" quantity of electric energy, or an "equivalent" quantity of heat makes its appearance, *and the ratios between the "equiva-*

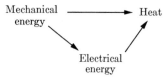

FIGURE 3

lent" quantities of the various species of energy form a single self-consistent set. This was first shown by the work of J. P. Joule who—in the period 1840–1850—established a solid experimental foundation for declaration of the conservation principle. Actually one of the first fruits of this work was a demonstration of just the case we have discussed, for Joule was able to show that from a given quantity of mechanical energy one obtains the same amount of heat by either of the routes shown in Fig. 3.

Suppose that into a system we convey a certain quantity of heat, q. This heat energy disappears from the surroundings and, as a result of the heat input, the system may do a certain amount of work, w, on the surroundings. But we may well find that the work so delivered by the system is less than the mechanical equivalent of the heat delivered to the system. Accepting the conservation principle, we must then suppose that energy equivalent to the difference $(q - w)$ is somehow stored in the system as an increase of "internal energy," and we write

$$q - w = \Delta E, \qquad q - w = dE. \tag{2}$$
For a finite change   For an infinitesimal change*

For the purposes of classical thermodynamics, either of the above equations is an entirely adequate definition of internal energy, but some may still wish to ask: What *is* the internal energy? Classical thermodynamics neither asks nor answers this query. On the atomic-molecular hypothesis we may imagine that the internal energy can be the kinetic energy of translational motion—which manifests itself in a rise of temperature of the system. Alternatively, we may imagine an increase in potential energy which does not show itself in a rise of temperature—as when the latent heat of vaporization increases the potential energy of particles without increasing their kinetic energies, or as when a heat of decomposition is stored as the potential energy of atoms or groups of atoms liberated from the bonds that formerly united them. But such speculations do not at all concern classical thermodynamics—which indeed derives much of its power and generality precisely from its ability to work effectively with the energy concept while making no more assumption about the "nature" of internal energy than about the constitution of matter.

---

* We will use q and w to symbolize, indifferently, both finite and infinitesimal quantities of heat and work respectively.

Characteristics of a Function of State. The change of internal energy corresponding to the transition from one state to another proves independent of the path taken between them. The situation is reminiscent of that obtaining for vertical displacements. Consider that I set out from the base of a mountain, at X, to climb—over very rough terrain—to its top at Y. Suppose that I can go by either route I or route II, as shown in Fig. 4. Along either route, I will be ascending more or less steeply at some times, traversing horizontally at others, and making longer or shorter descents at still others. In each phase of my journey I can determine (e.g., with an aneroid altimeter) my *net vertical ascent or descent for that phase*. Now, according to which route I choose, I will have two wholly different sets of components of ascent and descent. But *regardless of which route I choose*, arriving at last at Y I can write

Net vertical displacement $= \Delta h_{X \to Y}$

$$= \sum \text{Vertical ascents} - \sum \text{Vertical descents}.$$

That is, although the components will be entirely different along the two routes, the net vertical displacement is invariant—independent of the path taken. Note, too, that a return from Y to the starting point at X—along any path, say the more direct (aerial tramway) route R—completes the cycle and leaves nil vertical displacement:

$$\Delta h_{XYX} = \sum \text{Vertical ascents} - \sum \text{Vertical descents} = 0.$$

Consider now the analogous cycle involving ΔE, q, and w. Of course q and w are not vector quantities, like directional components, but analogy still obtains because, other things being equal, as defined by equation (2) ΔE is increased by any positive increment of q and decreased by any positive increment of w. Consider, then, that from state A of a system passage may be made by either route I or route II to some other state B thereof—whence a return to state A may be made via still a third route, R. For the complete cycle, restoring the original state, we must then write

$$\Delta E_{ABA} = \sum q - \sum w = 0.$$

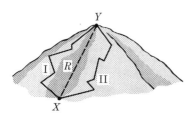

FIGURE 4

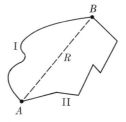

FIGURE 5

Were this not so, the ceaseless renewal of the cycle would yield a ceaseless net production or consumption of energy unlike anything ever yet encountered in the constantly increasing wealth of our experience. If we deny the last equation we deny a conservation principle we find well justified; if we accept the principle we must accept the equation.

Now the complete circuit can be made in either of two ways. Traveling from A to B over route I and returning via R, we have

$$\Sigma q - \Sigma w = q_I + q_R - w_I - w_R = 0,$$
$$= (q_I - w_I) + (q_R - w_R) = 0.$$

Traveling from A to B via route II, and again returning via R, we will have

$$(q_{II} - w_{II}) + (q_R - w_R) = 0.$$

Comparison of the last two equations makes it clear that

$$q_I - w_I = q_{II} - w_{II} \tag{a}$$

and that, therefore,

$$\Delta E_I = \Delta E_{II}.$$

Defined as $(q - w)$, ΔE has then—remarkably enough—a property that neither q nor w possesses. For ordinarily *both q and w are variables* depending on the path actually taken between A and B. This is most easily seen in a concrete example: consider as a system a container holding one mole of an ideal gas. Suppose a state A defined by pressure P_A and volume V_A, and a state B defined by pressure P_B and volume V_B. Given the ideal gas law

$$PV = nRT,$$

we have then sufficient specifications of state—for with $n = 1$ and P and V specified, only one value of T remains possible.* We can then represent the two states graphically, as shown in Fig. 6, and the two panels of that figure display two distinct routes for the transition from state A to state B.

Consider first the two-stage route shown in Fig. 6(a). In the initial stage the gas expands reversibly from volume V_A to volume V_B while, by constant input of heat, we maintain the pressure constant at its initial value P_A. In this stage the work done is $P_A(V_B - V_A)$. In the second stage we cool the gas at constant volume to the final pressure P_B—in which

---

* Remember that the value of R must vary with the units used to express P and V. For example, if liters and atmospheres are the units, then

$$R = \frac{(1 \text{ atm})(22.4 \text{ lit})}{(1 \text{ mole})(273°\text{K})} = 0.082 \text{ lit-atm/mole°K}.$$

The dimensions of R are those of energy/mole°K, and in other energy units R is ~ 8.3 joules/mole°K, ~ 2.0 cal/mole°K, etc.

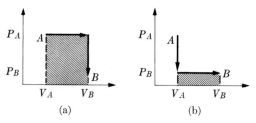

FIGURE 6

operation no $P \, \Delta V$ work is done because ΔV is zero. The net work is then $P_A(V_B - V_A)$, corresponding to the shaded area in Fig. 6(a).

Consider now the work done along the route shown in Fig. 6(b). The gas is first cooled at constant volume until it has the pressure P_B. It is then expanded reversibly to volume V_B, with a steady input of heat to maintain the pressure constant at P_B. In the first constant-volume stage no work is done; in the second stage the work is $P_B(V_B - V_A)$, corresponding to the shaded area in the second panel of Fig. 6. Since $P_A > P_B$,

$$w_{\mathrm{I}} = P_A(V_B - V_A) > P_B(V_B - V_A) = w_{\mathrm{II}}.$$

To the two different routes from A to B there correspond two different quantities of work and, in view of equation (a) above, there must be a further inequality in the heat terms:

$$q_{\mathrm{I}} > q_{\mathrm{II}}.$$

But ΔE, equal to $(q - w)$, depends only on the initial and final states concerned. Thus, for *all* paths from A to B,

$$\Delta E_{AB} = E_B - E_A.$$

The quantity E is a function of state: we can attribute to each thermodynamic state of a system a characteristic internal energy, E, that is independent of the way that state was arrived at.

Enthalpy. Save in galvanic cells, chemical reactions are ordinarily run under conditions in which only $P \, \Delta V$ work is possible. Let us now consider a change conducted *at constant volume*. Then $\Delta V = 0$, $P \, \Delta V = 0$, and $w = 0$. Equation (2) then reduces to just this:

$$\Delta E = q_V. \tag{3}$$

That is, when no work is done ΔE is simply equal to q_V, the heat liberated or absorbed under constant volume conditions. How can this possibly be so, when ΔE is a function of state and q varies with the path(s) chosen? Very simply: by stipulating maintenance of constant volume conditions we stipulate one particular path, in which case q, like ΔE, becomes a function only of the termini of the path.

The enforcement of constant volume conditions is often inconvenient, sometimes impossible. Ordinarily we run our reactions in systems maintained at constant pressure by contact with air or some other gas at atmospheric pressure. If q_P is the heat term under these conditions, if ΔV is the volume change accompanying the reaction, and if only $P \Delta V$ work is possible, then

$$\Delta E = q_P - w = q_P - P \Delta V. \tag{b}$$

If we call the initial state 1 and the final state 2, we can render the Δ terms as follows:

$$E_2 - E_1 = q_P - P(V_2 - V_1).$$

Rearranging, we have then:

$$q_P = (E_2 + PV_2) - (E_1 + PV_1).$$

This relation can be given exceedingly compact expression in terms of another thermodynamic function, the *enthalpy* (Gr. *enthalpein*, to warm in), or "heat content," symbolized by H and defined by the equation

$$H = E + PV. \tag{4}$$

The constancy of P was stipulated in deriving the equation before last; and that equation can now be rewritten as follows:

$$q_P = H_2 - H_1 = \Delta H. \tag{5}$$

The specification of constant pressure eliminates all but one path between the terminal states, which are, then, the sole determinants of q_P. Equation (5) assures us that this *must* be so for—defined in terms of E, P, and V—the enthalpy clearly *is itself* a function of state. To be sure, it lacks the significance of the genuinely fundamental state functions, energy and entropy, but it is a great operational convenience expressly designed to represent the heat liberated or absorbed under constant pressure conditions when only $P \Delta V$ work is possible.

Compare two states of a system in which *both* pressure and volume can vary. For the final and initial states, respectively, we write

$$H_2 = E_2 + P_2 V_2,$$
$$H_1 = E_1 + P_1 V_1.$$

Subtracting, we arrive at the following perfectly *general* equation:

$$\Delta H = \Delta E + \Delta(PV). \tag{6}$$

For the important *special* case in which P is stipulated constant, we take

P outside the Δ sign and write

$$\Delta H = \Delta E + P\,\Delta V. \tag{7}*$$

Depending on the sign of $\Delta(PV)$ in the general case, or the sign of $P\,\Delta V$ in the special case, ΔH may be either larger or smaller than ΔE. When gases are involved—and particularly when there is a change (Δn) in the moles of gas present—ΔH may differ substantially from ΔE. With effectively ideal gases at constant temperature we can write, for *both* the general and special cases,

$$\Delta H = \Delta E + (\Delta n)RT.$$

Thus, for example, when 1 mole of water is vaporized at 1 atm pressure at 100°C, then $\Delta H = 9.71$ kcal. Noting that the volume of the liquid vaporized (V_L) is essentially negligible compared with the volume of the gas produced (V_G), we have

$$P\,\Delta V = P(V_G - V_L) \doteq PV_G = (\Delta n)RT = (1)(2)(373) = 746 \text{ cal.}$$

And then:
$$\Delta E = 9.71 - 0.746 = 8.96 \text{ kcal.}$$

A corresponding calculation for the conversion of 1 mole of water to ice shows that in this case ΔE differs from ΔH by only 0.00004 kcal, which is negligible; and, in general, when only condensed phases are involved the changes of volume are small enough that $\Delta E \doteq \Delta H$ is ordinarily an excellent approximation.

Experimentally we cannot measure E's and H's as such, but only the *differences* ΔE and ΔH. However, *only those differences* are involved in statement and use of the first principle of thermodynamics. Hence (as with potential energies more generally) we are free to adopt, for the sake of convenience, some arbitrarily defined reference state relative to which ΔE's and ΔH's will be measured and stated. On one convention widely accredited by chemists, we take the enthalpies of the stablest forms of the chemical elements at 25°C and 1 atm pressure to be zero. That is, for all the elements, $H^0_{298} \equiv 0$. Here, as everywhere else, we use the subscript to indicate the absolute temperature to which the term refers and the superscript to indicate standard conditions (i.e., 1 atm pressure, 1 molar concentration for dissolved substances, etc.). Two further elements of convention connected with our usage of ΔE and ΔH terms may also be noted now. If nothing but $P\,\Delta V$ work can occur, we found $\Delta E = q_V$ and $\Delta H = q_P$. Since the q's (by convention) are positive when heat is added to a system and negative when heat is liberated (and lost) by a system,

---

* For a simpler, one-step derivation of equation (7), you have only to substitute from equation (5) in equation (b).

we see that ΔH, say, will be positive for an endothermic reaction and negative for an exothermic reaction (to which, indeed, should correspond a decrease in the "heat content" of the system). Finally, observe that, unlike the intensive property temperature, heat (and therefore also ΔE and ΔH) is an extensive property. That is, the amount of heat involved in a given change (and the ΔE or ΔH term corresponding to that change) is directly proportional to the size of the system involved. A figure for ΔE or ΔH is then meaningful only if we know the size of the system involved; in the absence of any other indication, a stated ΔE or ΔH will be assumed to refer to a change of one mole of material.

Thermochemistry and Hess's Law. The ultimate empirical basis of chemical thermodynamics is an immense body of thermal measurements made with any of a great variety of calorimeters. Because he usually works with constant pressures, the chemist works more with ΔH's than with ΔE's. The ΔH terms appertaining to any of a variety of physical and chemical changes—for example, vaporization, fusion, combustion, hydrogenation, solution, dilution, neutralization—are deeply involved in a variety of forecasting endeavors important to chemists (e.g., on page 85 we show that if the heat of reaction is known the effect of a temperature change on the equilibrium constant can be predicted quantitatively).

Sometimes we are anxious to learn the value of ΔH for a change which is difficult to measure in practice—for example, because the change is very slow; sometimes we wish to know ΔH for a change we are wholly unable to bring about in practice; and always we wish to extract, from a minimum series of measurements, ΔH values for a maximum series of different changes. Gratification of all these desires is achieved with the aid of Hess's law, the validity of which rests directly on the firm basis of the first principle of thermodynamics. Suppose we do not know (and, perhaps, cannot measure) ΔH_1 for the change from Q to R in Fig. 7. We can still *calculate* ΔH_1 if we have ΔH values for the changes Q to S, S to T, and T to R. Since H (like E) is a function of state, any two routes from A to B must give the same net ΔH. As a particular expression of Hess's law, we have then

$$\Delta H_1 = \Delta H_2 + \Delta H_3 + \Delta H_4.$$

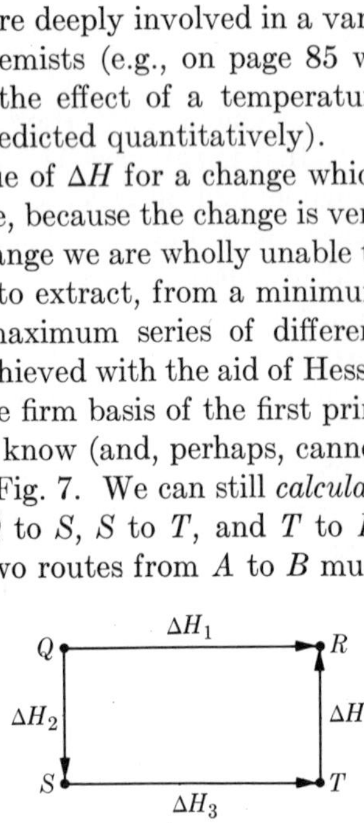

Consider a case in point: the calculation of ΔH for the reaction

$$C \text{ (solid)} + 2H_2 \text{ (gas)} = CH_4 \text{ (gas)}.$$

FIGURE 7

The parentheses enclose essential indications—usually abbreviated s, g, and (for liquids) l—of the physical state of the species involved in the reaction. When, as here, no more appears within the parentheses, we assume that the reaction has been run under standard conditions: at 298°K, 1 atm pressure, etc. A residual ambiguity can, however, be avoided by indicating explicitly that graphite is the particular solid allotrope of carbon that concerns us. Now the above reaction is unknown in practice but, with the aid of Hess's law, we can determine its ΔH from three combustion reactions easily accessible to study:

$$C \text{ (graph.)} + O_2 \text{ (g)} = CO_2 \text{ (g)}, \qquad \Delta H = -94.1 \text{ kcal;}$$
$$H_2 \text{ (g)} + \tfrac{1}{2}O_2 \text{ (g)} = H_2O \text{ (l)}, \qquad \Delta H = -68.3 \text{ kcal;}$$
$$CH_4 \text{ (g)} + 2O_2 \text{ (g)} = CO_2 \text{ (g)} + 2\,H_2O \text{ (l)}, \quad \Delta H = -212.8 \text{ kcal.}$$

We now multiply by 2 the second equation *and the ΔH term appertaining thereto*—for, unlike a potential (an intensive property), a change of enthalpy (an extensive property) depends on the quantity of material undergoing the change. And then, subtracting the third equation from the sum of the first two, we find

$$C \text{ (graph.)} + 2H_2 \text{ (g)} = CH_4 \text{ (g)}, \quad \Delta H = -94.1 + 2(-68.3) - (-212.8)$$
$$= -18 \text{ kcal.}$$

We thus establish the "heat of formation" of methane from its elements.

From a compilation of heats of formation—most of them calculated indirectly as above—we gain power to predict the heat terms for a multitude of reactions, on which no measurements need then be made. Thus, for example, if we know the heats of formation of 100 compounds any two of which can react with each other, to give products also included in the list of 100, we are in a position at once to calculate the heats of at least 4950 reactions. Consider a specific case:

$$CH_4 \text{ (g)} + Cl_2 \text{ (g)} = CH_3Cl \text{ (g)} + HCl \text{ (g).}$$

We earlier found CH_4 to have a heat of formation of -18 kcal; as an element, Cl_2 has, by definition, zero enthalpy; and the heats of formation for CH_3Cl and HCl are -20 and -22 kcal, respectively. Comparing the sum of the heat terms on the left of the equation $[-18 + 0 = -18]$ with the sum on the right $[-20 + (-22) = -42]$, we see that the materials on the right fall 24 kcal further below the norm of the free elements than the materials on the left. Thus 24 kcal must be liberated (and lost) in the reaction, for which, then, $\Delta H = -24$ kcal. The line of reasoning here followed through for a specific case is readily generalized to the reaction: $aA + bB = cC + dD$. Symbolizing the heat of formation of compound X as ΔH_{fX}, we have for the heat of reaction in the general case:

$$\Delta H = c\,\Delta H_{fC} + d\,\Delta H_{fD} - a\,\Delta H_{fA} - b\,\Delta H_{fB}.$$

For the completely general case, we represent by n_J the number of moles of each reactant, J, consumed, and by n_K the number of moles of each product, K, formed. For the reaction, as written, we then have

$$\Delta H = \sum n_K \, \Delta H_{fK} - \sum n_J \, \Delta H_{fJ}.$$

One can arrive at a predictive device even more strikingly efficient than a compilation of heats of formation, *if* one is prepared to overstep the bounds of thermodynamics in the region in which atomic-molecular theory borders it. But, as always when we leave the domain of thermodynamics, all gains in predictive power are made at the cost of predictive reliability. This point can be well illustrated through a brief digression from strictly thermodynamic considerations, to examine the predictive uses of a compilation of *bond energies*.

With the aid of Hess's law we can arrive at bond energies. But from the equation

$$\text{C (graph.)} + 2H_2 \text{ (g)} = CH_4 \text{ (g)}, \qquad \Delta H = -18 \text{ kcal},$$

we *cannot* at once conclude that the formation of a mole of C—H bond corresponds to the emission of $18/4 = 4.5$ kcal. Such an inference is invalid because in the above reaction we have not simply formed four C—H bonds; in addition we have broken two H—H bonds as well as the bonds that hold a carbon atom in graphite. Knowing the heat of dissociation of hydrogen and the heat of sublimation of graphite we can, however, proceed as follows:

$$\text{C (graph.)} + 2H_2 \text{ (g)} = CH_4 \text{ (g)}, \qquad \Delta H = -18 \text{ kcal};$$
$$\text{C (graph.)} = C \text{ (g)}, \qquad \Delta H = +172 \text{ kcal};$$
$$H_2 \text{ (g)} = 2H \text{ (g)}, \qquad \Delta H = +104 \text{ kcal}.$$

Multiplying the third equation by two, and subtracting the sum of it and the second equation from the first, we find

$$\text{C (g)} + 4H \text{ (g)} = CH_4 \text{ (g)} \qquad \Delta H = -18 - 172 - 208$$
$$= -398 \text{ kcal}.$$

Noting the presence in methane of four identical C—H bonds, we conclude that to break methane down to its component atoms we require an *average* investment of some 99 kcal per mole of bond broken. A C—H bond, we say, has a bond energy of 99 kcal. A similar computation, setting out from the heat of combustion of ethane, yields

$$2C \text{ (g)} + 6H \text{ (g)} = C_2H_6 \text{ (g)}, \qquad \Delta H = -677 \text{ kcal}.$$

Making due allowance for the presence of 6 C—H bonds (i.e., 6×99 kcal), we conclude that for a C—C link the bond energy is 83 kcal, and so on.

For the series of paraffin hydrocarbons the bond energies prove nicely additive. Wherever such additivity obtains we can, given the requisite bond energies, at once compute approximately the heats of reactions previously unmeasured, even when they involve compounds previously unprepared. Suppose we know that the bond energies of C—H, Cl—Cl, C—Cl, and H—Cl are 99, 58, 78, and 103 kcal, respectively, and suppose we wish to determine ΔH for the reaction

$$CH_4 \text{ (g)} + Cl_2 \text{ (g)} = CH_3Cl \text{ (g)} + HCl \text{ (g)}.$$

We see that this reaction involves the following changes:

breaking one	C—H bond:	$\Delta H =$	$+99$ kcal (endothermic)
breaking one	Cl—Cl bond:	$\Delta H =$	$+58$ kcal (endothermic)
making one	C—Cl bond:	$\Delta H =$	-78 kcal (exothermic)
making one	H—Cl bond:	$\Delta H =$	-103 kcal (exothermic)
	Net:	$\Delta H =$	-24 kcal (exothermic)

To the two significant figures, this is the same result we obtained from the heat of formation data.

If bond energies were always additive then—assuming that all the elements formed with each other only simple, single, covalent bonds—knowledge of the energies of the 4950-odd bonds formed between pairs of the 100-odd known elements would suffice for the calculation of the heats for all (gas-phase) chemical reactions already known or yet to be achieved. To support that calculation by the method of heats of formation we would, on the other hand, require a value for each of some half-million compounds already known. The method of bond energies is then extremely powerful, but it lacks the immense reliability of a strictly thermodynamic method. Double and triple bonds present no problem in principle for the bond-energy method; appropriate energies for them are easily obtained. But we now recognize that bonds between a given pair of atoms may have a different character in different molecules. Worst of all, we are forced to recognize that the fundamental assumption of additivity of bond energies fails badly in certain ("resonance") situations. The method of bond energies is then subject to all the uncertainties of molecular hypotheses while, however more clumsy in application, the strictly thermodynamic method based on heats of formation never fails.

Heat Capacity. The specific heat of a substance is the heat required to increase the temperature of 1 gm of the substance by 1°K. The heat capacity, C, is the heat required to increase the temperature of 1 gm-atom or mole of a substance by 1°K. Save at comparatively low temperatures, most heat capacities vary only very gradually with temperature. If C is

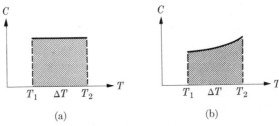

FIGURE 8

effectively constant over the temperature range concerned, the situation is as represented in Fig. 8(a). The heat required to increase the temperature of one mole of material from T_1 to T_2 is then represented by the shaded area, and is at once given by the equation

$$q = C(T_2 - T_1) = C \, \Delta T.$$

If C is insufficiently approximated by a constant, the situation is that represented in Fig. 8(b). The total heat required to produce the change from T_1 to T_2 is still the area under the plot of C vs. T, and this area can always be estimated graphically. However, if we possess an analytical expression for C as $f(T)$, the area is more easily and accurately found by integration:

$$q = \int_{T_1}^{T_2} C \, dT.^*$$

We have spoken of C as though it were a well-defined quantity, but of course the heat required to pass from one specified state of a system to another will vary with the path taken. The heat capacity can then *become* a well-defined quantity only by virtue of a specification of path. Actually, we find useful *two* species of heat capacities, corresponding to *two* simply specified paths—that at constant volume and that at constant pressure. *At constant volume* over a temperature range in which the heat capacity is constant, the first equation of this section becomes

$$q_V = C_V \, \Delta T.$$

But, in view of equation (3), we can then at once write

$$\Delta E = C_V \, \Delta T.$$

---

* For many substances C can be expressed by an empirical power series of the type $C = a + bT + cT^{-2}$. In such a case, for one mole of material, we will write

$$q = \int_{T_1}^{T_2} (a + bT + cT^{-2}) \, dT = a(T_2 - T_1) + \frac{b}{2}(T_2^2 - T_1^2) - c\left(\frac{1}{T_2} - \frac{1}{T_1}\right).$$

If, over the temperature range concerned, C_V is *not* constant, substitution in the second equation of this section yields

$$\Delta E = q_V = \int_{T_1}^{T_2} C_V \, dT.$$

All of these equations have been written for one mole of material, but the corresponding expressions for n moles are readily seen to be

$$\Delta E = n\int_{T_1}^{T_2} C_V \, dT \underset{\text{IF } C_V \text{ is constant}}{=} nC_V(T_2 - T_1) = nC_V \, \Delta T. \tag{8}$$

At constant pressure analogous expressions can be found by inspection. For one mole of material of constant heat capacity we have first

$$q_P = C_P \, \Delta T.$$

And, in view of equation (5),

$$\Delta H = C_P \, \Delta T.$$

If C_P varies over the temperature range concerned, then, substituting as before, we find

$$\Delta H = q_P = \int_{T_1}^{T_2} C_P \, dT.$$

Lastly, the general expression for n moles of material assumes this form:

$$\Delta H = n\int_{T_1}^{T_2} C_P \, dT \underset{\text{IF } C_P \text{ is constant}}{=} nC_P(T_2 - T_1) = nC_P \, \Delta T \tag{9}$$

For an ideal gas there is an attractively, and usefully, simple relation between C_P and C_V. When an ideal gas is heated at constant volume, no work is done, and all the heat invested goes into raising the temperature of the gas. When, however, the ideal gas is heated at constant pressure— although of course the same amount of heat is still required to raise the temperature of the gas—an *additional* investment of heat is required to provide for the $P \, \Delta V$ work done by the heated gas as, at constant pressure, it expands against the atmosphere. If, then, C_V is the heat required to increase the temperature of 1 mole of an ideal gas by 1°K at constant volume, and C_P is the corresponding quantity at constant pressure, we see that

$$C_P = C_V + P \, \Delta V.$$

The ideal gas law shows that, for a constant quantity of gas maintained at constant pressure, the variation of volume with temperature is

$$P \, \Delta V = nR \, \Delta T.$$

But, by the definition of "heat capacity," the quantity of material is

1 mole and the temperature interval is 1°K. Hence

$$P \, \Delta V = (1)R(1) = R.$$

Whence it follows that, *for an ideal gas,*

$$C_P = C_V + R. \tag{10}$$

This relation expresses the sole empirical basis that J. R. Mayer could find, 120 years ago, for his argument that work and heat are both species of a general "energy" that is conserved. Given the values of C_P and C_V for air (measured by Gay-Lussac and others), Mayer was able to estimate that one calorie is equivalent to 3.6 joules of mechanical work (modern value, ~ 4.2 joules).

Equation (10) has been abundantly confirmed for real gases at reasonably low pressures, and the heat capacity ratio

$$\gamma = \frac{C_P}{C_V} = \frac{C_V + R}{C_V}$$

offers an interesting criterion for distinguishing monatomic and polyatomic gases. Consider how this comes about. In deriving the ideal gas law from the kinetic-molecular theory, one of the important way-stops is the equation

$$PV = \tfrac{1}{3}Nmu^2.$$

Here the pressure P is supposed to be the result of the bombardment of the walls of a vessel by the N particles—each with mass m and average velocity u—present in the volume V. Multiplying both sides of the equation by $\tfrac{3}{2}$, we find

$$\tfrac{3}{2}PV = N(\tfrac{1}{2}mu^2).$$

If one mole of gas is present, N becomes Avogadro's number and the right side of this equation is seen to represent nothing more or less than the total kinetic energy of all the particles present. Now, for one mole of a perfect gas, we write

$$PV = RT.$$

Putting the last two equations together, we can at once conclude that $\tfrac{3}{2}RT$ represents the energy of translational motion of the molecules of one mole of any ideal gas at any temperature T.

Now consider one mole of an ideal monatomic gas heated at constant volume. We find no way in which the added energy can be disposed of save as an increment in the kinetic energy of the gas particles. For this gas we should then be able to calculate C_V *a priori;* it is nothing but the increment in the kinetic energy of one mole of gas particles consequent to a 1°K rise in temperature. Thus

$$\Delta \, \overline{\text{Kinetic energy}} = \tfrac{3}{2}R \, \Delta T = \tfrac{3}{2}R = C_V \doteq 3 \text{ cal/mole-deg.}$$

$$\text{For } \Delta T = 1°\text{K}$$

TABLE 1

HEAT CAPACITY RATIO OF GASES AT A PRESSURE OF 1 ATM

(T_{BP} = boiling point temperature)

Elements	γ
He, Ne, A (near 25°C)	1.67
Hg (near T_{BP} = 356°C)	1.67
Na (near $T_{BP} \doteq$ 880°C)	1.68
H_2, O_2, N_2 (near 25°C)	1.40
H_2O (near T_{BP} = 100°C)	1.32

With $C_V = \frac{3}{2}R$, equation (10) requires that $C_P = \frac{5}{2}R$, whence $\gamma = 1.67$. This result was actually predicted almost a decade before an experimental measurement was finally achieved (in 1876, for mercury vapor), and the *general* excellence of the agreement with experiment is readily seen from Table 1.

With a monatomic gas all the energy input goes into increasing the energy of translational motion. With polyatomic gases, on the other hand, part of the energy input is diverted into increasing the energies of rotational and vibrational motions—"degrees of freedom" wholly absent in monatomic gases. Due to this diversion, the total heat input that is required to produce the standard increment in kinetic energy corresponding to a 1°K rise in temperature is then greater for a polyatomic gas than for a monatomic gas; and the greater the number of degrees of freedom active in absorbing energy, the greater will be C_V and the smaller will be the ratio $\gamma = C_P/C_V = 1 + (R/C_V)$. Since all but the monatomic gases have such "extra" degrees of freedom fully operative at and above room temperature, $\gamma \doteq 1.67$ becomes a highly distinctive mark of a monatomic gas, and as such played an important role in the earliest characterization of the inert gases discovered at the close of the 19th century.

Kirchhoff's Equations. Consider the general reaction

$$aA + bB = lL + mM.$$

Suppose we have measured ΔH_1, the change of enthalpy for the reaction at some temperature T_1. Actually, to measure ΔH at some other temperature is then a work of supererogation if we have available to us values of C_P for the various reactants and products involved. Given such values— $(C_P)_A$, $(C_P)_B$, $(C_P)_L$, $(C_P)_M$—we can calculate ΔH_2 at any other temperature T_2 in terms of the lay-out shown in Fig. 9. Since H is a state function, the two paths must give the same net change in H. Therefore

$$\Delta H_1 = \Delta H_r + \Delta H_2 + \Delta H_p.$$

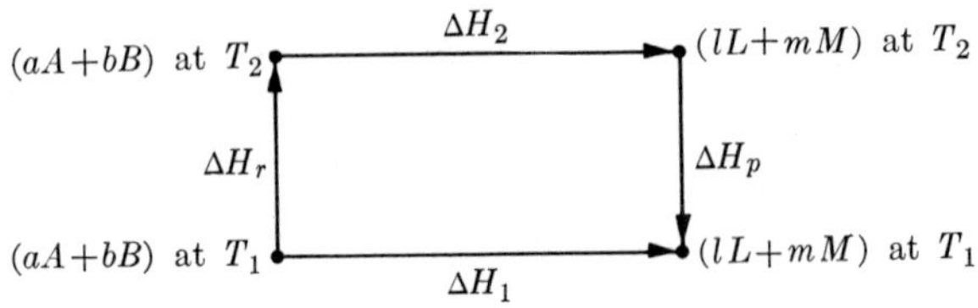

FIGURE 9

Assuming maintenance of constant pressure throughout the cycle, we observe that to carry the reactants from T_1 to T_2 we need

$$\Delta H_r = \int_{T_1}^{T_2} [a(C_P)_A + b(C_P)_B]\, dT.$$

Similarly, to return the products from T_2 to T_1, we must have

$$\Delta H_p = \int_{T_2}^{T_1} [l(C_P)_L + m(C_P)_M]\, dT.$$

Substituting these values and rearranging terms yields

$$\Delta H_2 = \Delta H_1 - \int_{T_1}^{T_2} [a(C_P)_A + b(C_P)_B]\, dT - \int_{T_2}^{T_1} [l(C_P)_L + m(C_P)_M]\, dT.$$

By inverting the limits of the second integral (and, correspondingly, changing its sign) we can combine terms to get

$$\Delta H_2 = \Delta H_1 + \int_{T_1}^{T_2} \{[l(C_P)_L + m(C_P)_M] - [a(C_P)_A + b(C_P)_B]\}\, dT.$$

Inside the integral sign appears the difference between the quantity of heat required to increase the temperature of all the products by 1°K and that quantity of heat required to increase the temperature of all the corresponding reactants by 1°K. Denoting by ΔC_P this over-all change in the heat capacity of the system, consequent to the reaction, we can then write

$$\Delta H_2 = \Delta H_1 + \int_{T_1}^{T_2} \Delta C_P\, dT. \tag{11}$$

This is Kirchhoff's equation for a change at constant pressure and, if ΔC_P is effectively constant over the range T_1 to T_2, it simplifies to

$$\Delta H_2 = \Delta H_1 + \Delta C_P(T_2 - T_1). \tag{12}*$$

---

* The corresponding equation for changes occurring at constant volume is

$$\Delta E_2 = \Delta E_1 + \int_{T_1}^{T_2} \Delta C_V\, dT \overset{\text{If } \Delta C_V \text{ is constant}}{=} \Delta E_1 + \Delta C_V(T_2 - T_1). \tag{13}$$

Following Kopp (1864), we find that at any temperature well removed from 0°K a given element has much the same heat capacity when bound in *any* of its solid compounds whatsoever and, if nongaseous, even when free. Were Kopp's law perfectly accurate and universally applicable, ΔC_P would always be zero. Because the law falls short of perfect accuracy and generality, ΔC_P's are finite, but ordinarily comparatively small. As a result, ΔH's usually change quite slowly with temperature, and can be taken as effectively constant over considerable temperature spans.

Explosions and flames. Given that ΔH and ΔE *do* change very significantly over *great* ranges of temperature, the calculation of peak temperature and pressure produced by an explosion may seem to pose an exceedingly difficult problem, but it is one that has an amusingly, and significantly, simple solution that can be applied also to the determination of the maximum temperature of steady-state flames, and so on. Consider, for example, a reaction in which the gases X and Y are brought together in the correct proportion to form gaseous Z by the strongly exothermic reaction $X + Y = Z$. Let it be given that at constant pressure the heat capacity of Z is $(C_P)_Z$ and, further, that the reaction is initiated at a temperature of 298°K, for which temperature we are given ΔH_{298} for the production of one mole of Z by the indicated reaction. We are now asked for the peak temperature attained when the reaction is run (i) at constant volume, in a sealed bomb to the walls of which we will assume no heat loss, and (ii) at constant pressure, as a steady-state flame formed by mixing streams of X and Y, with the heated gas doing work by expanding reversibly against (but, we will assume, losing no heat to) the surrounding atmosphere.

Even given the simplifying assumptions of no heat loss—and many more data—the above problems look pretty hopeless. As for (i), consider that the final temperature will be a function of a heat of reaction that changes progressively as the temperature rises with the advance of the reaction. Consider further that the actual temperature rise produced by any particular fraction of the heat released will depend on the heat capacity of the particular gas mixture then present, which will in turn depend on the extent to which the reaction has already proceeded. Part (ii) involves both these complications, and poses in addition the difficulty of estimating the work done against the atmosphere, which depends on the final volume and thus involves the (unknown) final temperature, and so on and on. From this exceedingly grim-looking set of interlocked variables we can, however, escape very easily—if we have but the wit to substitute, for the actual path of the reaction, another more readily analyzed. This is an expedient open to us whenever, as here, we can set up our problem in terms of variables of state. Instead of trying to follow the actual complex

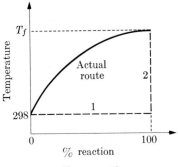

FIGURE 10

course of the reaction, we conceive it as occurring in two hypothetical stages, as indicated in Fig. 10. Each of these stages is individually tractable, and since they can be put together to connect the initial and final states, we can use the data given to us to establish the condition of the final state demanded of us.

Consider first problem (i). For a change at constant volume we do well to use ΔE rather than ΔH, and C_V rather than C_P. Given ΔH_{298}, equation (7) permits us to calculate ΔE_{298}; given $(C_P)_Z$, we readily find $(C_V)_Z$ by equation (10). Looking now at the diagram, we see that if ΔE_a is the difference between the initial and final states along the actual route, then, since E is a function of state,

$$\Delta E_a = \Delta E_1 + \Delta E_2.$$

But now we already know something about ΔE_a. At constant volume, by equation (3), $\Delta E = q_V$ and, since we have postulated no loss of heat to the walls of the bomb, $\Delta E_a = q_V = 0$. Consequently,

$$\Delta E_1 + \Delta E_2 = 0.$$

Consider now ΔE_1. Imagine that, by constant withdrawal of the heat formed, we contrive to run the reaction to completion at the initial temperature of 298°K. Then ΔE_1 will be nothing but $n\,\Delta E_{298}$—the number of moles of Z formed (n), multiplied by ΔE_{298}, which we already know. What about ΔE_2? Since, over-all, no withdrawal of heat from the system is permissible, in the second step we must (hypothetically) feed back into the system all the heat produced and (hypothetically) removed in the first step. The heat so reintroduced raises the temperature of the product gas Z to some final peak temperature, T_f. For the n moles of Z formed we have then, by equation (8), $\Delta E_2 = n(C_V)_Z(T_f - 298)$. Putting ΔE_1 and ΔE_2 together, we can then write

$$n\,\Delta E_{298} + n(C_V)_Z(T_f - 298) = 0, \qquad \text{or} \qquad (T_f - 298) = \frac{-\Delta E_{298}}{(C_V)_Z}.$$

Note that for an exothermic reaction ΔE is negative, so that the more strongly exothermic the reaction the greater will be the temperature rise $(T_f - 298)$, just as it should be.* We have then found an exceedingly simple solution to what seemed an exceedingly difficult problem—but when strongly exothermic reactions are involved we must take care not to *over*simplify. For example, $(C_V)_Z$ is unlikely to be constant over the great temperature range then involved, in which case $(C_V)_Z$ must be expressed as a function of temperature and an integration must be performed, as shown in the footnote on page 16. Moreover, if, at the calculated peak temperature, Z is very extensively dissociated into X and Y, this makes nonsense of the original assumption of 100% complete reaction. Although perfectly sound in principle, our simple formula cannot, then, be applied without some discrimination.

Given the above solution to part (i) of the problem, part (ii) presents no new difficulty. For the change at constant pressure we simply use ΔH and $(C_P)_Z$ where at constant volume we used ΔE and $(C_V)_Z$. As before, we write

$$\Delta H_a = \Delta H_1 + \Delta H_2.$$

At constant pressure $\Delta H = q_P$ and, given the stipulation of no heat loss,

$$\Delta H_2 + \Delta H_1 = \Delta H_a = q_P = 0.$$

The same reasoning and analogous substitutions then yield for the constant pressure case the equation

$$(T_f - 298) = \frac{-\Delta H_{298}}{(C_P)_Z}.$$

Subject to such limitations as those noted above, this useful equation permits us to calculate the maximum temperature attainable with a stoichiometric mixture of any reactants combining to form a single product.

Some Ideal Gas Calculations. Thermodynamic processes are often categorized as either "isothermal" or "adiabatic." In isothermal processes we permit (or contrive) whatever transfers of heat are required to keep the temperature of the system constant. At the other extreme, in a process that is adiabatic (Gr. *adiabatos*, *a*, not + *dia*, through + *bainein*, to go) no heat enters or leaves the system. We now discuss ideal-gas calculations under four main headings—obtained by subdividing each of the two major categories according to whether the change proceeds reversibly or irreversibly.

---

* Having found the peak temperature T_f, we easily find the peak pressure, P, if we are given V_B, the volume of the bomb, and n, the number of moles of Z formed. For then

$$P = \frac{nRT_f}{V_B}.$$

Isothermal changes. Imagine a volume V_1 of an ideal gas expanding isothermally into a vacuum to a final volume V_2. For the expansion against an external pressure of zero, $P \Delta V = 0$. For this expansion, then, $w = 0$, and also, as Joule found experimentally, $q = 0$.* By our first principle $\Delta E = q - w$ and, finding $q = w = 0$, we see that for the isothermal expansion of an ideal gas into a vacuum ΔE is *necessarily* zero. At first sight this seems a very strange conclusion. To be sure, if we imagine that the internal energy of the gas inheres in the translational, rotational, and vibrational motions of its particles, there is every reason to suppose that, at constant temperature, the internal energy *should* remain constant simply because the molecular motions should remain as energetic in a large as in a small volume. Yet, on the other hand, the expanded gas can no longer supply all the work recoverable from the compressed gas, and we feel that, somehow, the expanded gas *must* differ from the compressed gas. That feeling is perfectly correct, and we shall soon find a way of formulating the difference, but *the difference is not one of internal energy.*

For the expansion into vacuum of an ideal gas, we find $\Delta E = 0$. Since E is a function of state, this conclusion can at once be vastly generalized to *all* isothermal expansions (and compressions) of ideal gases. We have analyzed the peculiarly simple case of a vacuum expansion in which $q = w = 0$, but, for the isothermal expansion of an ideal gas from any particular initial volume V_1 to any particular final volume V_2, ΔE must be the same for all routes connecting the same initial and final states. As always, q and w will vary with the details of the actual route taken (e.g., with the magnitude of the external pressure), but with $\Delta E = 0$ along *all* routes, for *any* isothermal expansion or compression of an ideal gas we can write

$$q = w = \int_{V_1}^{V_2} P \, dV \underset{\text{IF } P \text{ is constant}}{=} P \Delta V . \tag{14}$$

I. *Isothermal irreversible change.* The work done by an expanding gas is determined by the external pressure, P_x.

EXAMPLE 1. One liter of an ideal gas at a pressure of 10 atm expands into a vacuum until its total volume is 10 liters. How much heat is absorbed and how much work is done in the expansion? We have

$$q = w = P_x(10 - 1) = 0(9) = 0.$$

No work is done; *no* heat is absorbed.

---

* Using more sensitive equipment, we now find that with real gases (having small but finite intermolecular attractions) small but finite magnitudes of q are experimentally detectable. But for an ideal gas (in which such attractions are, by definition, nil) q must also be nil.

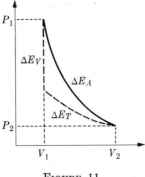

FIGURE 11

EXAMPLE 2. Consider the same expansion, but this time against a constant external pressure of 1 atm. We have

$$q = w = P_x(9) = 9 \text{ liter-atm} = 214 \text{ cal.}$$

II. *Isothermal reversible change* occurs under ideal conditions in which the external pressure never differs more than infinitesimally from the internal pressure, in which case the former may be represented by the latter. Substitution of the ideal gas law in equation (14) then yields

$$q = w = \int_{V_1}^{V_2} \frac{nRT}{V} \, dV = nRT \int_{V_1}^{V_2} \frac{dV}{V},$$

$$q = w = nRT \ln \frac{V_2}{V_1} = 2.3 nRT \log \frac{V_2}{V_1} = nRT \ln \frac{P_1}{P_2}. \qquad (15)$$

EXAMPLE 3. Consider the same expansion, to a final volume of 10 liters, conducted reversibly. Since $PV = nRT$, we know from the original conditions that $nRT = 10$ liter-atm. Substituting in equation (15), we then have

$$q = w = (2.3)(10) \log \tfrac{10}{1} = 23 \text{ lit-atm.} = 548 \text{ cal.}$$

Adiabatic changes. With no heat entering or leaving the system, any work performed by the system must be done at the expense of its internal energy, for with $q = 0$ by definition, equation (2) reduces to $-\Delta E = w$. Now we already know how to express w, as $\int P \, dV$, but it is not so obvious how we are to express $-\Delta E$ for an expansion in which neither pressure nor volume nor temperature is constrained to constancy. However, as always when we deal with a function of state, we can determine ΔE for the over-all change by summing (over a series of steps that lead to the same final state) ΔE's readily evaluated for steps expressly contrived to proceed under the constraints we find it convenient to impose. Imagine the adiabatic expansion resolved as shown in Fig. 11. In the first stage the ideal gas is cooled at constant volume to its final temperature T_2; in the second stage, with the reintroduction of all the heat hypothetically removed in the first, the gas expands isothermally to its final volume, V_2. For the over-all adiabatic change we then have that

$$\Delta E_A = \Delta E_V + \Delta E_T.$$

But in the immediately preceding section we found that the isothermal expansion of an ideal gas produces no change of internal energy, so that $\Delta E_T = 0$. And from equation (8) we already know how to evaluate ΔE_V. Consequently, for the adiabatic expansion of an ideal gas we write

$$\Delta E_A = n\int_{T_1}^{T_2} C_V \, dT + 0 = n\int_{T_1}^{T_2} C_V \, dT.$$

And now at last we can substitute in our *general* equation for adiabatic change, $-\Delta E = w$, to find for the *special* case of an ideal gas that

$$-\Delta E = -n\int_{T_1}^{T_2} C_V \, dT = \int_{V_1}^{V_2} P \, dV = w. \tag{16}$$

III. *Adiabatic irreversible change* is illustrated by two examples, in both of which we assume P_x and C_V constant.

EXAMPLE 4. Two moles of an ideal monatomic gas ($C_V = 3$ cal/mole·°K) expand irreversibly from an initial pressure of 10 atm, against a constant external pressure of 1 atm, until the temperature drops from the initial value of 325°K to a final value of 275°K. How much work is done, and what is the final volume? We have

$$-\Delta E = -nC_V(T_2 - T_1) = -(2)(3)(275 - 325) = 300 \text{ cal.}$$

In other units, the loss of internal energy is 12.6 liter-atm, and this must equal the work done in the adiabatic expansion. Hence

$$w = P(V_2 - V_1) = (1)(V_2 - V_1) = 12.6 \text{ liter-atm.}$$

We can then solve for V_2 as soon as we know V_1, and this last we can calculate from the perfect gas law (expressing R as 0.082 liter-atm/mole·°K) and the data given:

$$V_1 = \frac{nRT}{P} = \frac{(2)(0.082)(325)}{10} = 5.33 \text{ liters,}$$

and so
$$V_2 = 12.6 + 5.33 = 18 \text{ liters.}$$

EXAMPLE 5. An ideal monatomic gas ($C_V = 1.5R$) initially at 298°K and 10 atm pressure expands adiabatically and irreversibly until it is in equilibrium with a constant external pressure of 1 atm. What is the final temperature of the gas? We write

$$-\Delta E = -nC_V(T_2 - T_1) = P_2(V_2 - V_1) = w,$$

$$-n(\tfrac{3}{2}R)(T_2 - 298) = P_2\left(\frac{nRT_2}{P_2} - \frac{nR(298)}{P_1}\right),$$

$$-\tfrac{3}{2}(T_2 - 298) = \left(T_2 - \frac{(1)(298)}{10}\right),$$

and so
$$T_2 = 191°\text{K}.$$

IV. *Adiabatic reversible change* requires for its construal formulas we now derive, setting out from equation (16):

$$-nC_V \, dT = P \, dV = \frac{nRT}{V} \, dV,$$

$$\frac{dT}{T} = -\frac{R}{C_V} \cdot \frac{dV}{V}.$$

If, like R, C_V is constant, the integration is easy:

$$\ln \frac{T_2}{T_1} = -\frac{R}{C_V} \ln \frac{V_2}{V_1} = \frac{R}{C_V} \ln \frac{V_1}{V_2} = \ln \left[\frac{V_1}{V_2}\right]^{R/C_V}, \qquad \text{(c)}$$

so that
$$\frac{T_2}{T_1} = \left[\frac{V_1}{V_2}\right]^{R/C_V},$$

whence
$$T(V)^{R/C_V} = \text{constant.} \qquad (17)$$

A second relation can be derived from the equation preceding (17) by substituting on the left side of the equation with the aid of the perfect gas law $PV = RT$, and by reconstructing the exponent on the right side with the aid of equation (10). In that case,

$$\frac{P_2 V_2}{P_1 V_1} = \left[\frac{V_1}{V_2}\right]^{R/C_V} = \left[\frac{V_1}{V_2}\right]^{(C_P - C_V)/C_V} = \left[\frac{V_1}{V_2}\right]^{(\gamma - 1)},$$

whence
$$P(V)^\gamma = \text{constant.} \qquad (18)$$

EXAMPLE 6. Just 0.410 mole of a monatomic gas fills a 1-liter container to a pressure of 10 atm. It is expanded reversibly and adiabatically until a pressure of 1 atm is reached. What are the final volume and temperature, and what is the work done in the expansion? For a monatomic gas $\gamma = \tfrac{5}{3}$. Given (18), we have

$$(10)(1)^{5/3} = (1)(V_2)^{5/3}.$$

Cubing both sides of the equation, and then extracting the fifth root of

10^3, we find $V_2 = 4$ liters. Then

$$T_2 = \frac{P_2 V_2}{nR} = \frac{(1)(4)}{(0.410)(0.082)} = 119°\text{K}.$$

The same kind of perfect gas law calculation gives $T_1 = 298°\text{K}$, whence we calculate the work thus:

$$w = -\Delta E = -nC_V(T_2 - T_1)$$
$$= -0.410(3)(119 - 298) = 220 \text{ cal}.$$

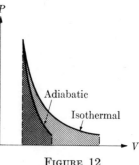

FIGURE 12

Compare Examples 3 and 6, both of which refer to the reversible expansion, to a final pressure of 1 atm, of 1 liter of gas at an initial pressure of 10 atm. As was already assumed tacitly in drawing Fig. 11, in the adiabatic expansion the pressure falls off more sharply than in the isothermal case, as shown in Fig. 12, due to the drop in the temperature of the gas. As a result, the isothermal expansion yields a greater final volume and a greater work output.

The Second Principle of Thermodynamics

We all have a feeling that, however drastic it may appear, in every change there is a "something" that remains constant. From the very beginning of the era of modern science, men (e.g., Descartes) have conceived that "something" as more or less close kin to what we would call energy. And energy—or, better, mass-energy—*is* surely conceived by us as a "something constant" enduring through all change. The first principle of thermodynamics thus gives quantitative expression to our firm conviction that "plus ça change, plus c'est la même chose."

We have another conviction scarcely less intense—the conviction that the future will not repeat the past, that time unrolls unidirectionally, that the world is getting on. This second conviction finds quantitative expression in a second principle of thermodynamics stipulating a new state function—entropy (Gr. *entrope;* from *en,* in + *trope,* turning)—which, by always increasing in the direction of spontaneous change, indicates the "turn" taken by all such change. Little more than a century ago Clausius first founded classical thermodynamics by developing some of the consequences of these two postulates:

> Die Energie der Welt ist konstant.
> Die Entropie der Welt strebt einem Maximum zu.

If a speeding lead bullet is stopped by an unyielding (and thermally insulated) sheet of armor, all the *kinetic energy* of the bullet is converted into *internal energy* that manifests itself in a rise of temperature. But we never find that equal bits of lead, heated to the same temperature, suddenly cool down and move off with the velocity of bullets, although such a development would be perfectly compatible with the first principle of thermodynamics. We find that the first principle of thermodynamics permits a great variety of changes never found in practice, and so leaves us an entirely excessive degree of latitude. As chemists we would like to predict the direction in which a reaction would proceed in reaching equilibrium, but either direction is equally compatible with the first principle. Only with the acquisition of a second principle can we put arrows into our equations before the reactions are tried.

We seek a criterion for predicting the direction of spontaneous changes. Everyday experience suggests certain special cases about which we have no doubt. When there are in practice differences in certain *intensive properties,* the spontaneous change is always that which eliminates the differences. If we have a difference of *pressure* on two sides of a piston, the piston moves spontaneously in the direction, and to the extent required, to yield equalization of pressures. If we have a difference of *temperature,* "heat flows" from the hot body to the cold body until the temperatures are equal. If we have a difference of *electrical potential,* charge passes in the direction, and to the extent required, to produce equality of potentials. And so on for differences of *concentration* (or, much better, "chemical potential") and the like.

Amply useful though these generalizations are, they are far from being everywhere sufficient. Most obviously, they offer us no means whatever for predicting the direction of spontaneous chemical reaction which may produce profound changes even in systems throughout which there reigns initially complete uniformity of pressure, temperature, electric potential, and concentration(s). One other possible clue may then suggest itself. In purely mechanical systems prediction of the direction of spontaneous change presents little difficulty: spontaneous change seems always to be of a nature, and in a direction, that reduces the potential energy of the system to a minimum. At one time it was thought that an analogous rule could be used to predict the direction of spontaneous chemical change: the spontaneous reaction is that which minimizes the heat content of the system. But today we recognize endothermic reactions that occur spontaneously, and so also exothermic reactions that do *not* occur spontaneously. We must then dig a great deal deeper to find an adequate criterion for the prediction of the direction (and extent) of spontaneous chemical change.

On Reversibility and Irreversibility. In thermodynamics, reversibility is a key concept that has a technical meaning transcending the idea of a change that can proceed in either direction. A reversible change is one so conducted that the system, and its surroundings, can at the end be restored to identically the same condition as at the outset. Once reversed, a reversible change is one that leaves no trace on the universe. In irreversible changes, on the other hand, attempts to restore the original conditions always leave some residual alteration, either in the system or in its surroundings. Some changes are irreversible in principle: the conversion to heat of the kinetic energy of mass motion is, we think, absolutely irreversible. Some changes (e.g., all the others mentioned in the preceding section) are reversible in principle, and the extent to which they are reversible in practice depends on just how they are conducted.

Consider the reaction

$$Zn \text{ (s)} + Cu^{++} \text{ (1M aq.)} = Cu \text{ (s)} + Zn^{++} \text{ (1M aq.)}.$$

If I simply throw zinc dust into aqueous copper sulfate the reaction is soon completed with the evolution (and dissipation) of heat, and the accomplishment of no work. Even if the heat is recovered and somehow applied (e.g., through a heat engine-dynamo combination) to reverse the above reaction, I find myself wholly unable to restore the system to its original state without leaving some change in its surroundings. Suppose now that, instead of conducting the reaction by direct mixing, we set up a Daniell cell. If we short-circuit the cell the same net reaction then takes place—again with no recovery of work, and with the evolution of the same amount of heat as before. Thus for a second time the reaction has proceeded irreversibly; but it *can* be conducted in a different, essentially reversible, manner.

Suppose that instead of short-circuiting the cell we use it to drive an electric motor which, perhaps through some arrangement of gears, stores energy by stretching a spring. Suppose further that we so contrive the motor that at all times its back emf is only *infinitesimally less* than the cell potential. Suppose all the systems to be ideal: free from mechanical friction, electrical resistance, and the like. Then if at any time we infinitesimally increase the tension of the spring, we can tap its mechanical potential energy to drive the motor in reverse, as a dynamo continuously adjusted to deliver to the cell an opposed emf *infinitesimally greater* than the cell potential. The reaction will be reversed and, supposing diffusion effects prevented, the cell and its immediate surroundings will be restored to their original state at the very instant that the spring resumes its original conformation.

The reversible arrangement we have described is obviously purely hypothetical—only an imaginary demonstration or *gedanken* experiment.

And the perfectly reversible change is only an ideal abstraction to which, fortunately enough, many realizable changes represent excellent approximations. The ideal motor-spring-dynamo rig for the recovery of the cell's energy is purely hypothetical, but the cell itself can, in practice, be studied under almost perfectly reversible conditions—with a potentiometer which measures the cell emf by opposing to it an externally generated emf so nearly equal that no detectable current enters or leaves the cell. The perfectly reversible change is then the unobservable ideal limit approached by some observable changes, and its role in thermodynamics is similar to— although almost infinitely more important than—the role played in classical mechanics by weightless, frictionless, ideal pulleys and the like.

We asserted, but did not prove, that when the reaction in the galvanic cell was conducted reversibly we would, in principle, be able to recover sufficient work to restore the cell and its surroundings to their original condition. Although in studies of the galvanic cell we make our closest approach to realizing in practice the ideal condition of reversibility, a demonstration that reversibility is possible in principle is far more readily given for a system much simpler than the galvanic cell. Consider the isothermal expansion of an ideal gas in a cylinder closed by a perfectly fitting but wholly frictionless piston. In Examples 1 through 3 (pp. 24–25) we determined the work done when 1 liter of gas at a pressure P_s of 10 atm expands isothermally, to a final volume of 10 liters, against an external pressure that had one of three possible magnitudes. For zero external pressure no work is done, as shown in Fig. 13(a). For one atmosphere external pressure some work is done, as shown in panel (b), but we readily see that a great deal more work could be extracted were we willing to readjust the external pressure from time to time, as shown in panel (c). Starting with a relatively high external pressure, we allow the gas to expand until the internal pressure equals the external pressure. At this point, in order to secure a further expansion, we somewhat reduce the external pressure. The gas again expands until its pressure matches the external pressure, at which point we again reduce the external pressure, . . . Now, although we recover more of the available work in (c) than in (b), *still* some is escaping us. But we recover an ever greater proportion of the available work the greater the number of steps through which we are prepared to take the external pressure. The greater the number of steps, the more closely does the step curve approach the smooth curve, and in the limit of an infinite number of infinitesimal steps the work obtained is just that included under the smooth curve, as shown in panel (d).

What about the recompression? By applying a steady external pressure of 10 atm, as shown in panel (e), we invest much more work than we have to. For, as shown in panel (f), much less work will be required if we are prepared to readjust the external pressure from time to time. We start

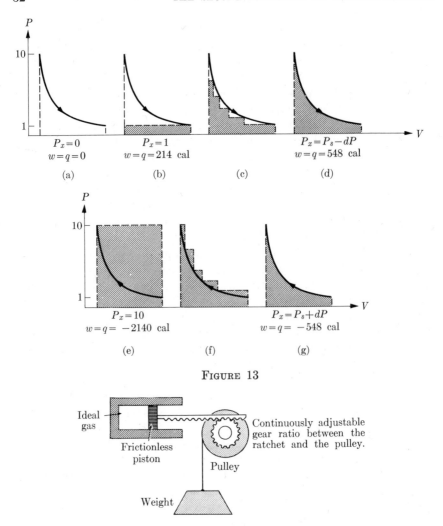

FIGURE 13

FIG. 14. An ideal engine.

with an external pressure only slightly greater than one atmosphere, and compress the gas until internal and external pressures become the same. At this point, to secure a further compression, we somewhat increase the external pressure; ... The greater the number of steps, the more closely does the step curve approach the smooth curve; and in the limit of an infinite number of infinitesimal steps the work required is just that included under the smooth curve, as shown in panel (g). Figure 14 shows schematically a hypothetical ideal device (after Sherwin) whereby the work delivered *by* the system, as in Fig. 13 (d), is stored in the lifting of a weight.

An infinitesimal addition made to the lifted weight causes it to descend to its initial position while delivering *to* the system just the work required for the reversible recompression, as in Fig. 13 (g). System and surroundings are thus restored to precisely their original states.

A reversible expansion, delivering the maximum amount of work, is attained only in the circumstance that an infinitesimal change in the external pressure (from $P_s - dP$ to $P_s + dP$) suffices to reverse the piston's movement. This suggests the essential condition for reversible change in general. When charge is drawn from a cell the maximum work is recoverable—and reversibility obtains—only when the emf opposing the current is just infinitesimally less than the cell voltage. An infinitesimal increase in the opposing emf then suffices to reverse the direction of the current. When heat is transferred from one body to another the process is reversible solely when T_1 is greater than T_2 only by the margin of dT, so that an infinitesimal rise in T_2 suffices to reverse the direction in which heat is transferred, and so on.

This condition for reversible change entails a cognate condition: a finite change conducted reversibly will require an infinite period for its completion. Under the impulse of a pressure difference dP, even an ideal piston moves at an infinitesimal rate. The rate of heat transfer will be infinitesimal when the temperature difference is infinitesimal. When the voltage of a galvanic cell is measured with a potentiometer, the emf's are so perfectly balanced that the essentially reversible transfer of charge need not exceed a rate of 10^{-9} amp, but it then requires the comparatively "infinite" period of 3×10^6 years for one mole of reaction to occur in the cell.* A truly reversible process is then an infinitely long succession of pseudo-equilibria, each of them never more than infinitesimally removed from a true equilibrium. It is indeed precisely through this resolution, into an infinite series of pseudostatic states, that change is brought within the scope of a classical thermodynamics which—with its exclusive concern for equilibrium state, and its rejection of considerations of path and rate—is perhaps better denominated thermo*statics*.

No observable process proceeding at a finite rate is truly reversible. This means that from no observable process do we recover the maximum work necessary to restore the initial state of the system and its surround-

---

* Reversibility is approachable *only* under such conditions. Joulean heating—the resistive heat dissipation that is the electric analog of frictional loss in mechanical systems—becomes negligible compared with the power recoverable from the cell only as the current $\mathscr{J}$ approaches zero. Representing resistance by $\mathfrak{R}$ and voltage by $\mathfrak{E}$, we have

$$\frac{\text{Power loss due to Joulean heating}}{\text{Power output}} = \frac{\mathscr{J}^2 \mathfrak{R}}{\mathscr{J} \mathfrak{E}} = \frac{\mathscr{J} \mathfrak{R}}{\mathfrak{E}} \rightarrow 0 \qquad \text{when } \mathscr{J} \rightarrow 0.$$

ings. Instead there is a progressive dissipation, or degradation into heat, of the other forms of energy. We learn to estimate the extent of this degradation by considering the extent to which heat can be retransformed into other species of energy, most notably into mechanical energy.

The Carnot Cycle. Heat and work terms we found variable according to the choice of route. However, assuming that only $P\,dV$ work is possible, we did find that, for a change made at constant volume, $q_V = \Delta E$, and for a change at constant pressure, $q_P = \Delta H$. Equal to changes in state functions, these q terms are well-defined quantities simply because when we specify that the change be made at constant volume, or at constant pressure, we specify one particular path and rule all others out of consideration. There is then but one possible q_V and one q_P. Now arises this question: If q_{rev} represents the heat liberated or absorbed in a reversible change from one state to another, is q_{rev} a well-defined quantity in the same sense that q_P and q_V are? The answer is no! When we stipulate a reversible change we stipulate only a *mode* of carrying on a change—which may still proceed along any of a number of paths to many of which correspond different values of q_{rev} and, thus, w_{rev}.[*] This point is best established by reference to a crucially important concrete case. Figure 15(a) and (b) show precisely how different amounts of work can be done in the reversible expansion of an ideal gas from one given state to another. In (a) the gas first expands isothermally from state A to state B, the latter being so chosen that a further adiabatic expansion carries the gas to state C. In (b), on the other hand, there is first the adiabatic expansion from A to D, where D is so chosen that a further isothermal expansion brings the gas to state C. Let all the changes be conducted perfectly reversibly. When we actually plot the curves corresponding to the equa-

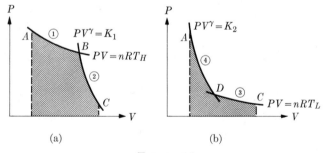

(a)   (b)

FIGURE 15

---

[*] In the case sketched in Fig. 13 there *was* a unique maximum value of w_{rev}, simply because in that case the stipulation of an *isothermal* change again excludes all but one path, and so of course all but one possible value for w_{rev} and for q_{rev}.

tions shown, we still find unmistakably different the areas enclosed between those curves and the V-axis. Clearly, different amounts of work are done along the different routes from A to C, and thus [since ΔE, equal to $(q - w)$, is the same for all routes from A to C] q_{rev} *does* vary from one path to another.

Almost a century and a half ago Carnot—by an ingenious combination of such adiabatic and isothermal changes—devised a theoretical engine with which the conversion of heat into work could be analyzed. Carnot actually chose the *simplest* combination of adiabatic and isothermal changes forming a closed cycle; his great *ingenuity* lay in the insight that the analysis he sought is readily attainable *only* with an engine that works in a closed cycle. The engine itself is in the same state at the end as at the beginning, and so undergoes no *net* change as heat is converted into work. We have then to consider only the changes produced, by the function of the engine, in its surroundings, and since these changes are readily calculable, we find ourselves in a position to deduce the maximum efficiency of a perfect heat engine functioning under defined conditions.

To attain a closed cycle of changes, we combine the two pairs of isothermal and adiabatic changes of an ideal gas shown in the Fig. 15. Consider these more carefully. In the first stage of (a) the reversible isothermal expansion, from A to B, performs the maximum possible amount of work, W_1,* against an external pressure ever infinitesimally less than the gas pressure. To maintain the temperature of the gas we transfer to it a quantity of heat Q_H* drawn from a large heat reservoir at a constant temperature T_H only infinitesimally greater than the temperature of the gas. In the second adiabatic stage of (a) no further heat is transferred, but the further amount of work, W_2, is done by the gas on its surroundings. In sum, the gas takes up heat Q_H at temperature T_H, and delivers the work $(W_1 + W_2)$ represented by the shaded area in the figure.

Consider now the pair of reversible changes represented in (b). Here we have first the adiabatic expansion from A to D: no heat is absorbed and, as work W_4 is performed, the temperature of the gas drops from T_H to T_L. In the further isothermal expansion the work W_3 is accomplished as the gas absorbs heat from a large reservoir at a temperature T_L. In sum, the gas takes up heat Q_L at temperature T_L, and delivers the work $(W_4 + W_3)$ represented by the shaded area in the figure. From the figure it is clear that

$$(W_1 + W_2) > (W_4 + W_3).$$

---

* To facilitate expression of a series of inequalities, for the rest of this section we will use Q to symbolize $|q|$, the absolute value of the heat term, and W to symbolize $|w|$, the absolute value of the work term. When the system gains heat or does work we will write Q or W; when the system loses heat or has work done on it we will write $-Q$ and $-W$.

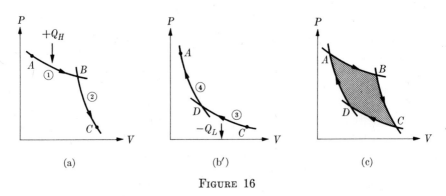

For the change from A to C, ΔE is a constant, so that the difference of the work terms necessitates that

$$Q_H > Q_L.$$

Two ways of combining changes (a) and (b), to give a closed cycle, will both be important to our consideration of Carnot's heat theorem. The first combination—yielding a heat engine—keeps (a) precisely as heretofore, but reverses the sense of (b) to that of (b'), shown in Fig. 16. Since both (b) and (b') are conducted reversibly, the figures for the heat absorbed and work delivered in the transition A-D-C will now reappear with opposite signs as the system passes in reverse, C-D-A. Thus to *compress* the ideal gas from C to D we *require* work of magnitude W_3 which, since it is now work *done on* the system, must be represented by the negative term $-W_3$. During this isothermal compression from C to D, heat numerically equal to Q_L is given up by the system to the heat reservoir at temperature T_L, and since this is heat *delivered by* the system it must be represented by the negative term $-Q_L$. For the further adiabatic compression from D to A we *require* the further input of work, $-W_4$.

Now imagine (a) and (b') combined as shown in Fig. 16(c). During the change A-B-C the gas absorbs heat Q_H and delivers work $(W_1 + W_2)$. During the change C-D-A the gas gives up heat $-Q_L$ and demands for its compression the work $-(W_4 + W_3)$. The *net* work done is

$$W = (W_1 + W_2) - (W_4 + W_3).$$

We have already seen that $(W_1 + W_2) > (W_4 + W_3)$. Therefore the above difference leaves a positive residue, W, which is the *net work delivered* around the cycle, represented by the (shaded) area enclosed within the cycle. The net heat is

$$Q_H - Q_L.$$

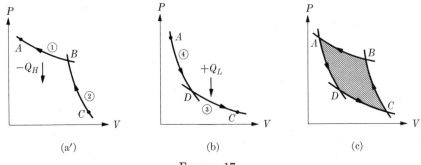

$$(a')$$ $$(b)$$ $$(c)$$

FIGURE 17

We have already seen that $Q_H > Q_L$; hence $(Q_H - Q_L)$ is positive, and there is a *net heat input*. The engine works in a closed cycle, and for it $\Delta E = 0$. Therefore, by the first principle, the net work output must equal the net heat input. That is,

$$W = Q_H - Q_L.$$

The efficiency of the engine can then best be expressed as the fraction of the total heat supplied it at high temperature which is converted to work. Thus

$$\text{Engine efficiency} = \frac{W}{Q_H} = \frac{Q_H - Q_L}{Q_H}. \qquad (19)$$

Consider now the second way in which the changes of Fig. 15(a) and (b) can be combined to form a closed cycle. This time we hold (b) to its original sense, and instead reverse the direction of (a) to give (a′). Combining (a′) with (b), as shown in Fig. 17, we arrive at a cycle which is that of a refrigerating machine. The change (a′)—traversing the route *C-B-A* —requires that the work $-(W_1 + W_2)$ be *done on* the system, and that the heat $-Q_H$ be *given up by* the system to the heat reservoir at temperature T_H. Combining (a′) with (b), we find that the net work involved is again that represented by the (shaded) area enclosed within the cycle, *but* the net work is now performed *on* (not *by*) the system. This net work is

$$-W = -(W_1 + W_2) + (W_4 + W_3).$$

The net work is represented by the negative term $-W$, since we already know that $(W_1 + W_2) > (W_4 + W_3)$. The net heat is

$$-Q_H + Q_L$$

and this is negative, since we already know that $Q_H > Q_L$. Indeed it *must* be negative: around the cycle $\Delta E = 0$, and the first principle of thermodynamics then requires that if net work is *done on* the system there must be an equivalent loss of heat *from* the system, as represented in the equation

$$-W = -(Q_H - Q_L).$$

The cycles of Fig. 16(c) and Fig. 17(c) differ only in the sense in which they proceed: in the second a net input of work causes the system to act as a refrigerator; in the first a net input of heat causes the system to act as a heat engine, with a net output of work. In both cases we have tacitly assumed an ideal gas as a working substance but, *whatever the working substance*, a combination of adiabatic and isothermal changes will always yield closed cycles to which all the previously derived relations must apply. Indeed, Carnot's central insight lies very close to this: the efficiency of an ideal heat engine depends on the boiler temperature, T_H, and the exhaust or condenser temperature, T_L, and is totally independent of the mechanism(s) of the ideal engine and the nature of the working substance(s) it may contain.

All ideal heat engines working between the temperatures T_H and T_L have exactly the same efficiency. We prove this statement by a species of *reductio ad absurdum.* Consider two ideal engines, P and P', both working between T_H and T_L, of which P is the more efficient. Let us now adjust the size of P' (perhaps changing the quantity of working substance it contains) until the work delivered per cycle by P' is the same as the work delivered per cycle by P. Now let us so couple P and P' that P, functioning as an engine, drives P' backward—as a refrigerator. In each cycle P draws heat Q_H at temperature T_H, rejects heat Q_L at temperature T_L, and does net work

$$W = Q_H - Q_L.$$

Correspondingly, by the investment of the work $-W'$ in each cycle, P' is made to draw heat Q'_L at temperature T_L and to deliver heat $-Q'_H$ at temperature T_H, and here

$$-W' = -(Q'_H - Q'_L).$$

Our prior adjustment of the sizes of P and P' assures that work consumption $-W'$ and work production W are perfectly balanced, so that

$$W - W' = 0.$$

Consequently, $(Q_H - Q_L) - (Q'_H - Q'_L) = 0$

and $$Q_H - Q_L = Q'_H - Q'_L. \tag{a}$$

Now we stipulated that P', functioning as an engine, has a lower efficiency than the engine P—whence equation (19) permits us to conclude that

$$\frac{Q_H - Q_L}{Q_H} > \frac{Q'_H - Q'_L}{Q'_H}. \tag{b}$$

Comparing equations (a) and (b), we see that

$$Q_H < Q'_H. \tag{c}$$

But then, in view of equation (a), it also follows that

$$Q_L < Q'_L. \tag{d}$$

Consider what these last two equations mean. Our coupled engine-refrigerator system involves zero net work delivered or consumed and, working in a closed cycle, has net $\Delta E = 0$. The only changes produced are then in the heat reservoirs, and they are truly remarkable changes. In view of equation (d) we see that the refrigerator draws more heat from the lower temperature reservoir at T_L than is delivered to that reservoir by the engine; in view of equation (c) we see further that the refrigerator delivers more heat to the high-temperature reservoir at T_H than is drawn from that reservoir by the engine. That is, the self-sufficient engine-refrigerator system—*drawing on no external source of work*—produces a flow of heat "uphill" from a cold to a hot body. But such a process is absolutely unknown to us, and is absolutely contrary to an immense body of experience that teaches us to expect the spontaneous flow of heat to be from hot to cold, and never the reverse. Observe too that a net flow of heat from a cold reservoir to a hot reservoir—with no net expenditure of work—would make it possible to pump heat from, say, the immense heat reservoir of the ocean, to a heat reservoir hot enough to drive an ordinary steam engine with its condenser at ocean temperature. But the many vain efforts to construct this ("second kind" of) perpetual motion machine lead us to suppose it utterly impossible.

We provisionally assumed that, working between the same temperatures T_H and T_L, ideal engine P' is less efficient than ideal engine P. We have found that this assumption leads ineluctably to two conclusions that experience teaches us to consider absurd. We therefore reject the provisional assumption, and so arrive at once at Carnot's heat theorem: all ideal engines working between the same temperatures T_H and T_L have the same efficiency. This being so, *any* ideal engine will serve for evaluation of that efficiency as a function of T_H and T_L—and we of course choose to make the evaluation with an engine containing, of all working substances, the most tractable theoretically: the ideal gas.

Let us take one mole of an ideal gas through the Carnot engine cycle shown in the accompanying Fig. 18.

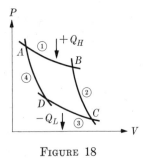

(1) In the first isothermal expansion $\Delta E = 0$, heat is absorbed, and work is delivered. Q and W, both positive, are then given by equation (15) as

$$Q_H = W_1 = RT_H \ln \frac{V_B}{V_A}.$$

FIGURE 18

(2) In the succeeding adiabatic expansion no heat is transferred and work W_2 is performed at the expense of a drop in internal energy, as set forth in equation (16):

$$W_2 = -\Delta E = -\int_{T_H}^{T_L} C_V \, dT.$$

(3) In the following isothermal compression again $\Delta E = 0$; work is *done on* the system and heat is given off from it. Q and W are then both negative, and are given by the equation

$$-Q_L = -W_3 = RT_L \ln \frac{V_D}{V_C}.$$

Since V_D is less than V_C, the right side of the equation turns out to be negative, as it should.

(4) In the final adiabatic compression work is again *done on* the system, and so the W term is again negative:

$$-W_4 = -\int_{T_L}^{T_H} C_V \, dT = +\int_{T_H}^{T_L} C_V \, dT.$$

In considering the whole cycle, the first thing we observe is that the work terms in stages (2) and (4) cancel out. We have then to consider only the heat and work terms involved in the isothermal stages (1) and (3). Since the whole operation in a closed cycle has net $\Delta E = 0$, the first principle of thermodynamics requires that the net work output equal the net heat input, or $W = W_1 - W_3 = Q_H - Q_L$. Substituting now in equation (19), we have

$$\text{Engine efficiency} = \frac{W}{Q_H} = \frac{Q_H - Q_L}{Q_H} = \frac{RT_H \ln \dfrac{V_B}{V_A} + RT_L \ln \dfrac{V_D}{V_C}}{RT_H \ln \dfrac{V_B}{V_A}},$$

$$\frac{Q_H - Q_L}{Q_H} = \frac{T_H \ln \dfrac{V_B}{V_A} - T_L \ln \dfrac{V_C}{V_D}}{T_H \ln \dfrac{V_B}{V_A}}.$$

Now a quite simple derivation* suffices to show that

$$\frac{V_B}{V_A} = \frac{V_C}{V_D},$$

and consequently that

$$\text{Engine efficiency} = \frac{W}{Q_H} = \frac{Q_H - Q_L}{Q_H} = \frac{T_H - T_L}{T_H}, \tag{20}$$

or

$$\frac{Q_H}{T_H} = \frac{Q_L}{T_L}. \tag{21}$$

Before turning to the broader implications of Carnot's work, which are read out of equation (21), consider briefly the bearing of this work on what most concerned Carnot: the efficiency of heat engines. Equation (20) tells us that

$$\frac{W}{Q_H} = \frac{T_H - T_L}{T_H}.$$

When the heat Q_H is delivered to an ideal engine, the latter returns us work W representing only a fractional conversion of the heat to work. A steam engine working between 127°C and 27°C has then as its absolute maximum possible (theoretical) efficiency:

$$\text{Efficiency} = \frac{W}{Q_H} = \frac{400 - 300}{400} = 25\%.$$

Precisely because heat engines are as inefficient as they are, heat pumps can be enormously advantageous. One might think that the most effective way of heating with electricity is a 100% conversion of electric energy into heat—for example, with resistance coils. But in principle (although, because of high capital costs, not always in practice) it is far more advantageous to use the electricity to drive a heat pump, i.e., a refrigerating machine that abstracts heat from the outside and delivers it at a higher

---

* Points B and C lie on the same adiabatic, and we can then substitute their values in equation (17):

$$T_H(V_B)^{R/C_V} = T_L(V_C)^{R/C_V} \quad \text{or} \quad \frac{T_H}{T_L} = \left[\frac{V_C}{V_B}\right]^{R/C_V}.$$

Points D and A also lie on the same adiabatic, and again we substitute in equation (17), to find

$$T_H(V_A)^{R/C_V} = T_L(V_D)^{R/C_V} \quad \text{or} \quad \frac{T_H}{T_L} = \left[\frac{V_D}{V_A}\right]^{R/C_V},$$

whence it follows at once that

$$\frac{V_C}{V_B} = \frac{V_D}{V_A} \quad \text{or} \quad \frac{V_C}{V_D} = \frac{V_B}{V_A}.$$

inside temperature. To drive this machine we must *invest work*, so that in the next to the last equation W will become $-W$, and now also we *deliver heat* at the higher temperature, so that Q_H becomes $-Q_H$. We have then

$$\frac{-W}{-Q_H} = \frac{T_H - T_L}{T_H}.$$

Suppose now that we pump heat from an outside temperature of $-18°C$ (0°F) and deliver it at an inside temperature of $+21°C$ (70°F). We have then

$$\frac{-W}{-Q_H} = \frac{294 - 255}{294} = \frac{39}{294} \doteq \frac{1}{7.5}.$$

That is, for every unit of energy invested as work we recover not just 1, but 7.5 units of energy delivered as heat.

The Concept of Entropy.   All ideal heat engines working between two given temperatures have the same efficiency, regardless of the working substance(s) they contain. In this circumstance Lord Kelvin grasped the possibility of creating a *truly absolute* scale of temperatures. The familiar ideal gas scale is obtained only by human selection of one particular group of (gaseous) thermometric substances, joined with an extrapolation to a humanly conceived abstraction: the hypothetical "perfect gas." These elements of human predilection are wholly absent from the scale of temperatures ($°\theta$) defined by rewriting equation (21)—which applies indifferently to all substances—in the form

$$\frac{Q_H}{\theta_H} = \frac{Q_L}{\theta_L}.$$

The ratio of the absolute θ temperatures is given by the ratio of the heats absorbed and rejected in any ideal Carnot engine, and $0°\theta$ is that limit of exhaust temperature with approach to which the engine approaches an efficiency of 1. Although gratifyingly absolute, the new scale does leave rather much to be desired in the matter of operational practicality. But we rejoice in the discovery that for all ordinary purposes the θ scale is excellently approximated by the ideal gas scale (T). In the gas thermometer we thus find united an operational convenience long taken for granted and a degree of absoluteness we could not before have assumed.

   The most important implication of equation (21) is the existence of a new variable of state: entropy. Consider the Carnot engine cycle shown in Fig. 19(c). There is an input of heat Q_H at temperature T_H and an output of heat $-Q_L$ at temperature T_L. Rearranging equation (21), we find that

$$\frac{Q_H}{T_H} + \frac{-Q_L}{T_L} = 0.$$

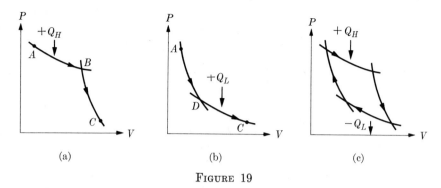

(a) (b) (c)

FIGURE 19

That is, for the closed cycle that returns the system to its initial state,

$$\sum \frac{q_{\mathrm{rev}}}{T} = 0,$$

where the subscript rev again reminds us that all the heat terms have been, *and must be,* measured under reversible conditions. Now a net change of 0 for the closed cycle that returns the system to its starting point is just what we found in the case of the internal energy, E; and precisely what we would demand of any other function of state. Let us then, hopefully, define a new function of state—the entropy, S—by means of the equation

$$dS = \frac{q_{\mathrm{rev}}}{T}.$$

Entropy will increase when heat passes into a system (for q_{rev} is then positive), decrease when heat passes out of a system (for q_{rev} is then negative), and thus around the closed circuit of the Carnot cycle we have

$$\Delta S = \sum \frac{q_{\mathrm{rev}}}{T} = 0.$$

Is S *really* a variable of state? We earlier observed that q_{rev} differs along different paths from one given state to another. But if S is a variable of state then, unlike q_{rev} itself, q_{rev}/T must remain the same along different reversible routes from one given state to another. Surprisingly enough, this is indeed the case. Observe (a) and (b) of Fig. 19. Passing from A to C along the route ABC, the system absorbs heat Q_H at temperature T_H; passing along the route ADC it absorbs heat Q_L at temperature T_L. Now $Q_H \neq Q_L$ but, by the terms of equation (21),

$$\frac{Q_H}{T_H} = \frac{Q_L}{T_L}.$$

Consequently ΔS, equal to q_{rev}/T, is indeed the same by either route.

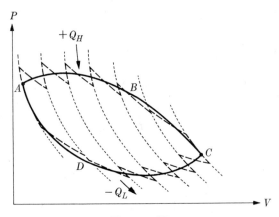

FIGURE 20

Does entropy continue to function adequately as a variable of state in changes that do not fit the Carnot pattern of successive adiabatic and isothermal stages? In Fig. 20 the smooth heavy line represents a cyclic change produced in *any* substance—gas, liquid, or solid—by *any* series of heat exchanges, even over entire continuous *ranges* of temperature. We lace the figure with a set of *adiabatics*, representing the adiabatic behavior of the particular working substance concerned, and then draw, again for that substance, the fragments of the *isotherms* that best approximate the indicated cycle. The closer the adiabatic lacing with which we begin, the closer will be the approximation to the original smooth curve, which is indeed the limiting outline attained when the adiabatic and isothermal segments become infinitesimal in length. We thus reduce the perfectly general cycle to the composite of a set of infinitesimal Carnot cycles, and the rest is easy.

Consider a change that carries the system reversibly from state A via B to C. In each infinitesimal isothermal section of its path the system *absorbs* some heat Q_H at some temperature T_H. The sum of all the infinitesimal increments—involving, presumably, different individual values of Q_H and T_H—we represent as

$$\sum_{ABC} \frac{Q_H}{T_H}.$$

If now the system is returned from C via D to its initial state A, then in each isothermal section of its path it *rejects* some amount of heat $-Q_L$ at some temperature T_L, and the sum of all the (presumably different) infinitesimal terms is

$$\sum_{CDA} \frac{-Q_L}{T_L}.$$

Now we arrive at the crux of the argument. Although the individual values of Q_H, T_H, Q_L, and T_L vary from one infinitesimal section to the next, observe that each pair of (Q_H, T_H) values along the route ABC falls opposite a pair of $(-Q_L, T_L)$ values along the route CDA—and in every case these are the *matching pairs* for the opposite isotherms of an infinitesimal Carnot cycle. To *each* such matching pair we can apply equation (21); hence for the *sum* of all the matching pairs it follows that

$$\sum_{ABC} \frac{Q_H}{T_H} + \sum_{CDA} \frac{-Q_L}{T_L} = 0.$$

And so, around the *general* cycle, as around the special Carnot cycle, we find that

$$\Delta S = \sum_{ABCDA} \frac{q_{\text{rev}}}{T} = 0.$$

With zero change for the closed cycle, entropy again comports itself as a proper state function.

One obvious corollary of the above demonstration may still be worth remarking. Proceeding as before from A via B to C, the system *absorbs* increments of heat, and for the whole change

$$\Delta S_{ABC} = \sum_{ABC} \frac{Q_H}{T_H}.$$

Proceeding *instead* from A via D to C, the system will now also *absorb* infinitesimal increments of heat, $+Q_L$, and for the whole change

$$\Delta S_{ADC} = \sum_{ADC} \frac{Q_L}{T_L}.$$

But now *exactly* the same argument of matching pairs, taken together with equation (21), permits us to conclude that

$$\Delta S_{ABC} = \sum_{ABC} \frac{Q_H}{T_H} = \sum_{ADC} \frac{Q_L}{T_L} = \Delta S_{ADC}.$$

And so, for the *general change* from state A to state C we find ΔS invariant with path. Entropy, defined by the equations

$$\Delta S = \frac{q_{\text{rev}}}{T}, \qquad\qquad dS = \frac{q_{\text{rev}}}{T} \qquad (22)$$

For a finite change at constant temperature   For an infinitesimal change

is a thermodynamic function: its changes depend only on the initial and final states of a system, and not on the paths taken between states.

What is entropy? There is a first principle of thermodynamics involving energy, a second involving entropy. Feeling that we know what energy *is* we ask what entropy *is*. But now, in point of fact, do we actually know what energy *is*? The classical dichotomy is matter-energy, and energy may then be defined as whatever produces heat. But when the dichotomy matter-energy breaks down, as it did at the beginning of the 20th century —when mass and energy proved interconvertible—then to that question what *is* energy we can give only the unsatisfactory answer that it *is everything*. Yet whatever our uncertainty about what energy is, that uncertainty does not in the least impair the thermodynamic usefulness of the energy concept. However obscure the concept of entropy may or may not prove, a knowledge of *how* the entropy concept *functions* permits us to use it to advantage however unsure we may be of what entropy is.

For the purposes of classical thermodynamics we need say no more than that the internal energy E is a function of state defined by the equation $dE = q - w$, and this is a statement of the first principle. And for the purposes of classical thermodynamics we need say no more than that the entropy S is a function of state defined by the equation $dS = q_{rev}/T$, and this is a statement of the second principle. Some have argued that the urgency of our quest for a "something constant" in all change leads us to *invent* the concept of energy and to enforce it as a convention. But the fact that, however q and w may vary individually, the difference $(q - w)$ is a constant for any given change of state—*that is a discovery*, providing a firm empirical footing for the first principle. Conceivably one might equally argue that the urgency of our quest for a "something pointing" the direction of all spontaneous change drives us to *invent* the concept of entropy. But the fact that, however q_{rev} and T may vary individually, the quotient q_{rev}/T is a constant for a given change of state—*that is a discovery*, providing a firm empirical footing for the second principle.

We do not need to know what energy *is*, but we find it satisfying and instructive to *interpret* internal energy, on the kinetic-molecular hypothesis, as the kinetic and potential energies of atoms and molecules. We do not need to know what entropy *is*, but we find it satisfying and instructive to *intrepret* entropy, on the kinetic-molecular hypothesis, in terms of the randomness of the distribution of atoms and molecules in space and in energy states. A peculiarly simple example of the complex concept of randomness is found in the previously cited case of a bullet abruptly stopped by a sheet of armor plate. The gross kinetic energy of the bullet disappears, and in its place appears thermal energy manifested in a rise of temperature of the bullet, which we suppose corresponds to an increased vigor of *random* motion of the lead atoms comprising the bullet. *Before* the impact all these atoms had, superposed on their random thermal motions, a single common directed component of motion as a result of which all the atoms traveled together as a group with the velocity of the bullet. *After* the impact this common component of motion is *randomized:* the motion of the bullet as a whole vanishes, but all the atoms comprising the bullet acquire an increased energy of random motion which we call heat. On this molecular picture we readily understand how it is that, although a moving bullet, when stopped, becomes heated, a stopped bullet, when heated, does not embark on motion. This asymmetry or unidirectionality grows out of a statistical situation amply familiar from everyday experience: for example, a new deck of cards, factory-packed in a regular arrangement of suits and denominations, is readily randomized by shuffling; but we consider it extremely improbable that by further shuffling we will soon bring the deck back to its original highly ordered arrangement.

We arrive here at a pointer in the direction of spontaneous change. All spontaneous processes seem to take place in that direction yielding some (often quite subtle) increase in disorder, and the direction becomes *predictable* as that for which there is an increase in entropy (positive ΔS) calculable in advance.* In all that follows we will interpret increase in entropy as correspondent to, or a reflection of, some increase in what Gibbs called "mixed-up-ness." But it cannot be too strongly emphasized that in classical thermodynamics the usefulness of the entropy concept is entirely independent of all such interpretation(s). This *must* be so for, as already noted, thermodynamics owes its peculiarly high reliability to its independence of all hypotheses about the nature of matter, energy, etc.

Evaluation of Entropy Changes. We never need to know what entropy *is* to calculate, from the equation $dS = q_{rev}/T$, the entropy changes associated with certain processes. If the given process is irreversible (e.g., the impact of the bullet, the solidification of a supercooled liquid, the expansion of a gas into a vacuum), we of course obtain no value of q_{rev} from which to determine ΔS. We seek then to conceive some path whereby, often by a coordinated series of steps, the same final state is achieved reversibly and (whether actually measured experimentally or, as is more

---

* One may, to be sure, find a *system* in which ΔS for a spontaneous change is negative. But what counts in these predictions is the sign of the *net* ΔS for the total change in the *aggregate* of the system and its environs. In a truly isolated system spontaneous change *always* proceeds with positive ΔS; and in the *aggregate* of nonisolated system and its environs the spontaneous change is, again, *always* that proceeding with positive net ΔS. Living systems will then constitute no exception. Plants are highly ordered arrays formed from less highly ordered nutrients like CO_2 and H_2O, but this gain in organization comes about only through an input, and degradation, of solar energy. Animals grow and acquire their own characteristic organization(s) only through a simultaneous degradation of the highly ordered arrays of atoms in the foods they draw, directly or indirectly, from plants.

usually the case, simply calculated) $\sum q_{rev}/T$ for these steps yields the value
of ΔS for the irreversible process.

Take as the simplest of possible examples the isothermal expansion of
an ideal gas into a vacuum. In passing from an initial volume V_1 to a
final volume V_2, the n moles of gas change wholly irreversibly—doing *no*
work and absorbing *no* heat. But, since S is a function of state, the value
of ΔS for this expansion is exactly the same (and thus readily calculable)
as the value of ΔS for the reversible isothermal expansion of the n moles
of ideal gas from V_1 to V_2. For *this* expansion equation (15) furnishes a
value of q_{rev} that permits us to write

$$\Delta S = \frac{q_{rev}}{T} = nR \ln \frac{V_2}{V_1} = nR \ln \frac{P_1}{P_2}. \tag{23}$$

If, for example, the volume of one mole of ideal gas is doubled isothermally,
then
$$\Delta S = 2.3nR \log \frac{V_2}{V_1} = (2.3)(1)(2) \log 2 = 1.38 \text{ cal/°K.}$$

Were the expansion in any degree irreversible both the work done and the
heat absorbed, q_{irr}, would to that degree be less than for the reversible
expansion and here, as everywhere, the relation that obtains is

$$\frac{q_{rev}}{T} = \Delta S > \frac{q_{irr}}{T}.$$

Of this relation, so peculiar at first sight, Mahan properly remarks that:
"The situation here is similar to that encountered with ΔH: ΔH is independent of the path, but is equal to q only when the process is carried
out at constant pressure. The entropy change is independent of path, but
is equal to q/T only when the process is carried out reversibly."

Observe that in the twofold isothermal expansion we begin with one
volume of ideal gas and one volume containing no gas, and we end with
the gas distributed evenly through the two volumes. The increase in
entropy corresponds to the increased "spread" of the system in space.
That the "spread" system is by far the less ordered or more probable arrangement is perhaps clearest if we consider the likelihood that at some
time we will again find one volume void and the entire gas reassembled
in the original volume V_0. The probability that one given molecule will
be found in V_0 is clearly $\frac{1}{2}$—just as the probability that a tossed coin will
fall heads up is $\frac{1}{2}$. The probability that a given second molecule will be
found in V_0 is also $\frac{1}{2}$, and the probability that both molecules will simultaneously be present in V_0 is $(\frac{1}{2})^2 = \frac{1}{4}$—just the probability that two
tossed coins will both fall heads up. For three of either molecules or coins
the probability is $(\frac{1}{2})^3 = \frac{1}{8}$, and so on. Given N distinguishable objects,

each of which can fall in either one of two categories, we find that the total number of possible arrangements is 2^N, and the probability of that single configuration in which all fall in the same category is then $1/2^N = (\frac{1}{2})^N$.

Consider now that in one mole of ideal gas there are 6×10^{23} independent particles. As we open the stopcock between two equal vessels—one containing gas and the other void—we have then every reason to expect the spontaneous spreading of the gas throughout the two volumes. Among all the possible configurations we have made accessible to the gas, the probability of that one configuration in which the gas remains, or comes again to re-collect itself, in the original one volume has the almost inconceivably minute value of $(\frac{1}{2})^{6 \times 10^{23}}$. This is, of course, only a stupendous improbability—not an impossibility—and it affords us some glimpse of what Gibbs was the first to recognize: the essentially statistical nature of the second principle of thermodynamics. But for any macroscopic specimen the balance of probability is so immense that we can say with perfect confidence that the spontaneous change will always be in the direction of that lower order or greater "spread" to which corresponds the calculated increase in entropy. Or, to pick a quite different case, the spontaneous equalization of temperatures in a bar hot at one end and cold at the other is a "spreading" process accompanied by an increase in entropy, and the spontaneous reconstitution of the initial distribution of temperature we have never observed and never expect to observe.

Gases expand spontaneously to fill their containers; they do not recompress themselves spontaneously. We can of course recompress the gas to its original state, and so bring about a *non*spontaneous process by the investment of work. The restoration of the original state demands some *reduction* of entropy attainable only by the *expulsion* from the system of heat $q_{rev} = T \,\Delta S$. Observe, however, that such a decrease in the entropy of the system entails a corresponding increase in the entropy of the surroundings (heat *lost* from the system is always heat *gained* by the surroundings). We may exploit this tie-up if ever we have trouble conceiving of a reversible route permitting evaluation of q_{rev}/T for some given irreversible process. For almost always we can easily hit upon a reversible route for the *opposite* change—starting from the final state and *restoring the original state* of the system. In this reversible change the (calculable or measurable) increase in the entropy of the system's surroundings is precisely equal to the increase in entropy accompanying the original irreversible change in the system.

As so far defined, only the changes of entropy, or differences of entropy content, are calculable. This is, of course, entirely analogous to the situation previously encountered in the cases of energy and enthalpy. In those cases "absolute" values of E or H could be computed only relative to reference states selected by convention. In the case of entropy a less arbitrary choice of reference state is possible. If entropy increases with heat input, we may think to approach a "natural" zero of entropy when, by removing as much heat as we can, we approach 0°K. We take the entropies of the pure well-ordered crystalline elements to be 0 at 0°K and, supported by a third principle of thermodynamics,* we also maintain that any pure compound in a fully ordered crystalline condition has at 0°K an entropy $S_0^0 = 0$. To find S_{298}^0—the "absolute" entropy of a mole of an element or compound in its standard state at 298°K—we have then only to determine the entropy change consequent to warming it from 0°K to 298°K, for then

$$\Delta S = S_{298}^0 - S_0^0 = S_{298}^0.$$

If the material is a crystalline solid with the same structure at 298°K as at 0°K we have simply

$$S_{298}^0 = \Delta S = \frac{q_{rev}}{T} = \int_0^{298} \frac{C_P \, dT}{T}.$$

At temperatures approaching 0°K, C_P falls off sharply towards zero, and in this region q_{rev}/T is usually estimated graphically on a plot of C_P/T vs. T extrapolated to 0°K. At higher temperatures C_P can usually be expressed as an analytical function of T, so that the last equation can be integrated, and if at any time C_P becomes effectively constant we can write for that region

$$\Delta S = C_P \int_{T_1}^{T_2} \frac{dT}{T} = C_P \ln \frac{T_2}{T_1}. \tag{24}†$$

Suppose that the substance melts before it reaches 298°K. At the melting point T_M melting is a reversible process, and q_{rev} is simply the heat of fusion ΔH_{fus} (positive, of course, because heat must be put *into* the system). Hence

$$\Delta S_M = \frac{\Delta H_{fus}}{T_M}. \tag{25}†$$

Using $(C_P)_s$ and $(C_P)_l$ to denote heat capacities of the solid and of the liquid respectively, we will then write, for one mole of a substance melting before 298°K is reached,

$$S_{298}^0 = \int_0^{T_M} \frac{(C_P)_s \, dT}{T} + \frac{\Delta H_{fus}}{T_M} + \int_{T_M}^{298} \frac{(C_P)_l \, dT}{T}.$$

---

* Like the two more familiar principles, the third also rests on experience, for it can be shown a necessary consequence of our repeated experience and firm conviction that, although indefinitely approachable, 0°K is unattainable.

† When, instead of constant pressure, constant volume conditions are stipulated, the sole change required in equations (24) through (27) is the replacement of C_P by C_V, and the replacement of ΔH terms by the corresponding ΔE terms.

If the substance boils before reaching 298°K then, considering that equation (25) offers a model formula for all reversible phase transitions, we will have

$$S^0_{298} = \int_0^{T_M} \frac{(C_P)_s \, dT}{T} + \frac{\Delta H_{\text{fus}}}{T_M} + \int_{T_M}^{T_B} \frac{(C_P)_l \, dT}{T}$$

$$+ \frac{\Delta H_{\text{vap}}}{T_B} + \int_{T_B}^{298} \frac{(C_P)_g \, dT}{T}. \qquad (26)\dagger$$

Given the third principle of thermodynamics, and the requisite data on C_P's and heats of fusion, vaporization, transition, etc., we can then calculate S^0_{298} values for elements and compounds. From these, in turn, we can calculate ΔS^0_{298}, the entropy change for a chemical reaction conducted under standard conditions at 298°K. For the general reaction

$$aA + bB = cC + dD$$

we will have simply

$$\Delta S^0_{298} = c(_C S^0_{298}) + d(_D S^0_{298}) - a(_A S^0_{298}) - b(_B S^0_{298}).$$

Suppose that, having so determined ΔS^0_{298}, we wished to know ΔS^0 at some other temperature. Simplifying only to the extent of assuming no phase changes between 298° and T, a derivation entirely analogous to that yielding (Kirchhoff's) equation (12) yields here

$$\Delta S^0_T = \Delta S^0_{298} + \int_{298}^T \frac{\Delta C_P \, dT}{T}. \qquad (27)\dagger$$

As remarked earlier, in discussing the variation of ΔH with temperature, ΔC_P is usually a comparatively small quantity. Consequently, like ΔH^0 values, ΔS^0 values for reactions usually change comparatively gradually with changes in temperature.

As a crystalline solid is heated there is a striking increase in entropy, equal to $\Delta H_{\text{fus}}/T_M$, at its melting point. Such a major increase is, of course, just what we should expect, since in melting the regular lattice array of the crystal is broken down to the much less highly ordered arrangement of corpuscles in a liquid. A further (and, usually, much larger) increase in entropy, equal to $\Delta H_{\text{vap}}/T_B$, takes place as the concentrated and still appreciably structured array of corpuscles in the liquid passes over into the highly dispersed, essentially random array of corpuscles in the gas phase. In this last case the increase in entropy seems to be comparable from one case to another. Trouton's rule coordinates heat of vaporization and boiling temperature in the empirical relation

$$\frac{\Delta H_{\text{vap}}}{T_B} \doteq 21.$$

That is, for a considerable variety of liquids, vaporization is accompanied by an increase of entropy approximating 21 cal/mole·°K. But regrettably the "constant" in this empirical rule is far from perfectly constant; it varies from ∼18 for O_2 boiling at 90°K to 23.24 for zinc boiling at 1180°K. However, our association of entropy and "spread" suggests a way to improve on Trouton's rule.

When we vaporize a mole of material at its boiling point then, although we work at a uniform pressure of one atmosphere, the one mole of material is spread over very different volumes, according to the magnitude of the boiling point. A mole of oxygen vaporized at its normal boiling point of 90°K is spread over only ∼7.4 liters; while at *its* normal boiling point of 1180°K a mole of zinc is spread over a volume more than ten times as great. Thus, over and above entropies of vaporization that possibly are constant, the Trouton rule involves entropies of expansion that certainly differ sharply. To improve the constancy of the Trouton "constant" we should then seek to evaluate the entropy change consequent to vaporization under conditions giving a more nearly constant "spread" of the gas phase. Hildebrand's rule works with whatever is the heat of vaporization, ΔH_{hv}, at that temperature, T_h, at which a liquid has a vapor pressure corresponding to the (arbitrarily chosen) standard concentration of 0.005 mole of substance per liter. Then

$$\frac{\Delta H_{hv}}{T_h} \doteq 27.$$

Here the "constant" is much more nearly constant, varying from 27.6 for oxygen to 26.4 for zinc. To be sure, there are still some exceptions: for water and ammonia the "constant" is close to 32. But this is precisely what we would expect once we know something of the nature of water and ammonia. Due to "hydrogen bonding" (reflected in their abnormally high melting and boiling points) water and ammonia are abnormally associated, and structured, even in the liquid phase, so that for them vaporization corresponds to a greater than average loss of order, and so to a greater than average increase in entropy.

If increase in entropy (and disorder, or "spread") is the *sine qua non* of a spontaneous process, how is it possible for a liquid, once vaporized, ever to recondense, or for a solid, once fused, ever to recrystallize spontaneously? Consider the second case more closely: certainly as the system resumes the ordered structure of the solid it *rejects* heat numerically equal to the heat of fusion ΔH_{fus}, and so *decreases* its entropy to the extent $-\Delta H_{fus}/T_M$. But recall that all heat lost by the system is heat gained by the surroundings which, if the crystallization is to proceed at a finite rate, must stand at an average temperature T *less than* T_M. Hence, for the entire unit (system + surroundings), we have

$$\Delta S = \frac{-\Delta H_{\text{fus}}}{T_M} + \frac{\Delta H_{\text{fus}}}{T} = \Delta H_{\text{fus}} \left[\frac{T_M - T}{T T_M} \right] > 0.$$

With *net* $\Delta S > 0$, the recrystallization will proceed spontaneously. And yet—yet—we may not be fully satisfied. Although the heat terms force us to recognize a *net* increase in ΔS, in the system we *see*—in the growth of the highly ordered crystals of the solid—a change we can regard as corresponding to an entropy *decrease*; but in the surroundings we may see *no* vestige whatever of the increased disorder or spread that should correspond to the entropy increase $+ \Delta H_{\text{fus}}/T$, allegedly numerically larger. The general point so raised is worth exploring further.

When a mole of a substance with a finite heat capacity (for simplicity assumed constant) is heated, without phase change, from temperature T_1 to temperature T_2, it undergoes an entropy increase $\Delta S = C \ln (T_2/T_1)$. In terms of what change can we interpret this increase? To be sure, if the substance expands when heated there is some spatial spread to which must correspond some increment of entropy. For such a substance $C_P > C_V$, and equation (24) can then be applied to compute the *difference* in the entropy increases occurring when one mole of a given material is heated through the same temperature interval at constant pressure and at constant volume:

$$\Delta S_P - \Delta S_V = (C_P - C_V) \ln \frac{T_2}{T_1}.$$

Although substantial in the case of gases, for which $(C_P - C_V)$ is comparatively large, the spatial spread is a much less significant contributor to the increase in entropy accompanying the heating of solids and liquids, and such spread can contribute *nothing* when the heating is conducted under (or calculated for) constant volume conditions. For all that, to the increase of entropy there *still* corresponds an increase in spread, but here spread of a species much more subtle than the purely spatial spread earlier noted.

With rising temperature the molecules of a substance heated at constant volume and with no phase change "spread" by distributing themselves over a greater range of energetic states. A particularly vivid illustration of this effect is provided in Fig. 21, which shows the distribution of translational energies in an ideal gas at three different temperatures. At low temperature comparatively large fractions of the molecules present are found in a comparatively small range of accessible energy states. As the temperature rises, however, more and more higher energy states become accessible to more and more molecules—which so spread themselves that only a com-

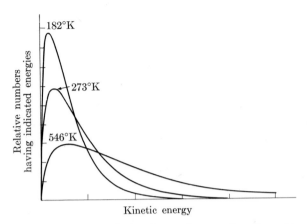

FIG. 21. Distribution of translational energies as a function of temperature.

paratively minute fraction of those present will be found in any small range of energies. To this spread of translational energies will correspond an increment in entropy, and we become able to account for the full magnitude of the entropy increase consequent to heating at constant volume and structure when, in addition to the spread in translational energies, we allow also for the spread in the energies of rotational, vibrational, and other degrees of freedom. An example of the progressive spread in vibrational energies is shown in Table 2. For a solid at low temperature the rise of entropy with increasing temperature is *entirely* a matter of the spread into higher vibrational energy levels. On this spread Einstein founded an early theory of low-temperature heat capacities that was one of the first important successes of Planck's quantum hypothesis.

The adiabatic expansion of an ideal gas provides a pretty illustration of both species of "spread" so far noted. If the expansion is conducted reversibly, $q = q_{rev} = 0$, and then $\Delta S = 0$. This comes about because the entropy *increment*, due to the increased spread of the molecules in space, is perfectly compensated by the entropy *decrement* due to the decreased spread of the molecular energies at the lower temperature assumed by the gas as a result of its expansion. Imagine this adiabatic process conducted in the two stages shown in Fig. 11 (page 25). In the first stage the gas is cooled reversibly at constant volume (V_1) and the entropy decrement due to this cooling is indicated by equation (24) to be $C_V \ln (T_2/T_1)$. In the second stage, of what is stipulated to be an adiabatic process, precisely the quantity of heat removed in the first stage must be reintroduced as the gas is expanded reversibly at constant temperature (T_2), and the entropy increment due to this expansion is given by equation (23) as

TABLE 2*

Number of the vibrational level	Fraction of the molecules of gaseous NO in each vibrational level as a function of temperature in °K				
	300	600	1000	2000	5000
0	0.9999	0.9886	0.9311	0.7344	0.4020
1	0.0001	0.0113	0.0640	0.1936	0.2373
2	0.0000	0.0001	0.0046	0.0521	0.1413
3		0.0000	0.0003	0.0143	0.0848
4			0.0000	0.0040	0.0513
>4				0.0016	0.0833

* Data of Johnston and Chapman reproduced, by permission, from *J. Am. Chem. Soc.* **55**, 153 (1933).

equaling $R \ln (V_2/V_1)$. But rearrangement of equation (c) on page 27 at once tells us that for the over-all adiabatic process

$$C_V \ln \frac{T_2}{T_1} + R \ln \frac{V_2}{V_1} = 0.$$

In the reversible adiabatic process the entropy increment due to increase in one species of spread is just counterbalanced by the entropy decrement due to decrease in another species of spread. In the irreversible adiabatic process this perfect compensation no longer obtains. Consider the mole of ideal gas expanding as before from volume V_1 to volume V_2. To the same increase in spatial spread will correspond the same entropy increment as in the reversible expansion. But in the irreversible expansion the gas does less work, loses less internal energy, and so will be found to have at the end of the expansion a temperature greater than T_2.* To the smaller temperature drop in the irreversible expansion will correspond a smaller decrement in the spread of molecular energies, and to that in turn an entropy decrement insufficient to neutralize the increment due to spatial spread. The irreversible process, though adiabatic, still shows positive ΔS: the heat transfer is nil, but it is now $q_{irr} = 0$ and, since $q_{rev} > q_{irr}$, $q_{rev} > 0$, so that *necessarily* $\Delta S > 0$. On this note we may do well to close a section in which we have everywhere *discussed* entropy changes in kinetic-molecular terms, but have everywhere *determined* entropy changes in terms of q_{rev}/T. The interpretations of entropy changes may afford us intellectual satisfaction (and, when developed quantitatively, they have an important role in statistical mechanics) but classical thermodynamics

* This is precisely what we *did* find: compare Examples 5 and 6, on pages 26–28.

is completely independent of how we may or may not choose to *interpret* changes in the state function, entropy, which we always *calculate* from the definition $dS = q_{rev}/T$.

Consequences of the Thermodynamic Principles

The principles are the seed; now we reap some part of the harvest: the prediction and/or rationalization of an immense number of regularities, scientific laws discoverable in experience. Let us review the crucial part of the argument so far given on which this further development will be founded. For a given change of state a system undergoes a fixed change ΔE, independent of the path and manner of the change. For a given path of change, the reversible manner of proceeding yields a work output w_{max} to which must correspond a maximum heat input q_{rev}:

$$\Delta E = q_{rev} - w_{max}. \tag{28}$$

Failing complete reversibility along *any* path, we obtain work, w, less than w_{max} for that path, and—since ΔE is fixed—the heat input q_{irr} must be less than q_{rev} for that path. Since S, like E, is a function of state, ΔS for a given change remains the same whatever the path and however reversibly or irreversibly it is traversed. Consequently, if by definition

$$\text{For a reversible process} \quad \Delta S \equiv \frac{q_{rev}}{T},$$

it follows that

$$\text{For an irreversible process} \quad \Delta S > \frac{q_{irr}}{T}.$$

Now reversibility is an ideal limit often approached but never attained in any observable change. All "natural" changes—those actually occurring spontaneously in the real world—are to some degree irreversible. All such changes take place in a finite (and, usually, quite brief) period, whereas they would require infinite times were they to proceed with the delicate balance of infinitesimally different opposing "forces" required for truly reversible changes. All observable changes being then to some degree irreversible, with q values somewhat less than q_{rev}, it follows necessarily that *for any observable change $\Delta S > q/T$*.

The only systems found in nature that do meet the criterion of reversibility are systems in equilibrium. Says Caldin:

Reversible change is characterized by an infinitesimal difference of intensity factors [pressure, temperature, electric potential, etc.] between system and surroundings:

$$I_{syst} - I_{surr} = \pm dI.$$

Equilibrium is defined by equality of these intensity factors:

$$I_{syst} - I_{surr} = 0.$$

These two equations are indistinguishable . . . *Any sufficient condition for reversibility is therefore also a sufficient condition for equilibrium.*

The better the approximation to reversibility attained in the conduct of some particular change, the more nearly will q/T approach ΔS. In the limit we arrive at an equilibrium system which is the infinitely enduring limiting case of reversible change that would by definition involve an infinitely prolonged series of states differing only infinitesimally from true equilibrium states. *For the limiting state of equilibrium, $\Delta S = q/T$.*

We have now arrived at the two essential criteria, for they are just these:

$$\text{For an observable change} \quad \Delta S > \frac{q}{T}, \tag{29}$$

$$\text{For equilibrium} \quad \Delta S = \frac{q}{T}. \tag{30}$$

Though *fundamental*, these relations are not yet reduced to their most useful forms. The involvement of q is doubly unfortunate. For one thing, it brings into the criteria a term not itself a function of state. Secondly, since a heat *transfer* necessarily involves both the system and its environs, these criteria can refer only to the aggregate of system and environs. This inconvenient linkage we dissolve by reexpressing the fundamental criteria in terms of two new thermodynamic functions of the state of a system.

Free Energy and Equilibrium. The first of the new functions is the Helmholtz free energy, or work function, symbolized by A (*Arbeit*) and defined by the equation

$$A = E - TS. \tag{31}$$

Defined entirely in terms of functions of state, A also is a function of state. Now compare two states of a system held at constant temperature:

$$A_2 = E_2 - TS_2,$$
$$A_1 = E_1 - TS_1.$$

Subtracting, we arrive at an important general relation for any change at constant temperature:

$$\Delta A = \Delta E - T \Delta S. \tag{32}$$

Substituting from equation (28), we have then

$$\Delta A = q_{\text{rev}} - w_{\text{max}} - T \Delta S.$$

But since $\Delta S = q_{\text{rev}}/T$, we see that

$$\Delta A = T \Delta S - w_{\text{max}} - T \Delta S = -w_{\text{max}},$$

whence $\qquad -\Delta A = w_{\text{max}}. \tag{33}$

For any given change *at constant temperature*, however otherwise we may elect to conduct that change, there *is* a maximum extractable work, expressible as the difference of a function of state, $-\Delta A$.

To find, in terms of A, criteria for determining the direction of spontaneous reaction, and the situation at equilibrium, we again set out from equation (32) for any isothermal change. Now, however, we do *not* stipulate a reversible change, but substitute for ΔE the *general* case expressed in the first principle of thermodynamics:

$$\Delta A = \Delta E - T \Delta S = (q - w) - T \Delta S.$$

Stipulating that only $P\,dV$ work is possible, and that the system is maintained at constant volume, we reduce w to zero. Hence

$$\Delta A = q - T \Delta S.$$

Now bring to bear the two fundamental criteria expressed in equations (29) and (30). For any observable change $T \Delta S > q$. Therefore for *every* observable change at constant temperature and volume there is a decrease of the Helmholtz free energy.

The criterion of a spontaneous change at constant T and V: $\qquad \Delta A < 0. \tag{34}$

At equilibrium, by equation (30), $T \Delta S = q$.

The criterion of equilibrium in a system at constant T and V: $\qquad \Delta A = 0. \tag{35}$

In the special circumstances indicated spontaneous change always reduces the capacity of the system to do work, and equilibrium is reached only when that capacity has been reduced to a minimum. Here then we have a function that can represent the changes and equilibria of chemical systems in much the way that the concept of mechanical potential energy represents change and equilibrium in purely mechanical systems. Consider a reaction of the following type: $G + H = L + M$. We prepare a plot

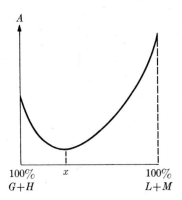

FIG. 22. Variation of free energy with composition of reaction mixture.

showing on one side the total value of A for the reactants G and H, on the other side the total value of A for the products L and M, and in between the values of A for the various mixtures of G, H, L, and M corresponding to different degrees of completion of the reaction. The curve obtained is usually of the type shown in Fig. 22, and the equilibrium composition is that represented by x, where, in the trough of the curve, the equilibrium defined by the condition $\Delta A = 0$ (better, $dA = 0$) is at last established when A assumes its minimum value. If the reaction proceeds at a finite rate in either direction, its progress from any initial condition to equilibrium is then a matter of "sliding down to the bottom."

Every system not at equilibrium is potentially capable of delivering work, but no system at equilibrium is capable of furnishing any work whatsoever. The *maximum* work *output* recoverable from the change represented in Fig. 22 is given by the vertical drop—that is, by $-\Delta A = A_{\text{initial}} - A_{\text{equil}}$, and this same quantity of work is indicated as the *minimum input* required for the nonspontaneous change (with $\Delta A > 0$) in which the initial state of the system is restored after it has reached equilibrium. In practice, of course, no change is ever strictly reversible, so that the maximum work is never recovered in any actual process. But, since A is a function of state, the value $-\Delta A$ for a given change is always the same—however much work is or is not recovered. Although the total *energy* of system and surroundings remains constant, every spontaneous change—to the extent that it is irreversible—must result in a degradation of energy: an irrecoverable decrease in the amount of ("free") energy available to do work.

Substituting from equation (33) in equation (32), we find

$$w_{\text{max}} = -\Delta E + T \, \Delta S.$$

Here we see the relation of the maximum work output to the diminution in internal energy. *If ΔS is positive* for the given change, the maximum work output is *greater* than the diminution in internal energy by the margin of $T \Delta S = q_{rev}$, where q_{rev} is heat *absorbed* by the system. Thus, for example, in the reversible isothermal expansion of an ideal gas there is *no* diminution in internal energy, and the work output is simply equal to the heat input. On the other hand, *if ΔS is negative* for the given change, the maximum work output is *less* than the diminution in internal energy by the margin of $T \Delta S = q_{rev}$, where q_{rev} is now heat *released* by the system. The heat so rejected corresponds to the heat rejected at exhaust temperature by a Carnot engine, and $T \Delta S$ is here the measure of the *unavailable energy*. Thus, for example, if an isothermal reaction at constant volume involves the formation of product molecules with structure(s) having a degree of organized complexity greater than that of the reactant molecules, then that reaction has negative ΔS and, of any drop in internal energy, only the difference $(-\Delta E + T \Delta S)$ is extractable as useful work, i.e., recoverable *"free energy."*

The criteria in terms of ΔA, exemplary for changes at constant temperature and constant *volume*, do not fully meet the needs of chemists, who most often conduct their reactions under conditions of constant temperature and constant *pressure*. For these conditions the essential criteria are better expressed in terms of the Gibbs free energy, F, defined by the equation

$$F = H - TS. \tag{36}$$

A development paralleling that which yielded equation (32) yields here, for a change at constant temperature,

$$\Delta F = \Delta H - T \Delta S. \tag{37}$$

Assuming constant pressure, we can substitute for ΔH from equation (7), which gives

$$\Delta F = \Delta E + P \Delta V - T \Delta S.$$

Substituting from equation (32), we have then

$$\Delta F = \Delta A + P \Delta V,$$

whence, in view of equation (33), we can conclude that

$$-\Delta F = w_{max} - P \Delta V = w_{net}. \tag{38}$$

Dismissing the work done against the atmosphere (seldom easily recoverable in chemical changes) the maximum "net work" obtainable from an isothermal change is then represented by $-\Delta F$. In any actual change the net work recovered will be less than $-\Delta F$ but, since F is a function of state, $-\Delta F$ for a given change remains the same however much work is or is not recovered.

Let us now express in terms of F the criteria of direction of spontaneous reaction and position of equilibrium. At constant temperature and pressure we have already found that

$$\Delta F = \Delta E + P \Delta V - T \Delta S.$$

Substituting now the *general* requirement of the first principle of thermodynamics for any change, reversible or irreversible, we obtain

$$\Delta F = (q - w) + P \Delta V - T \Delta S.$$

Stipulating now that only $P \Delta V$ work is possible, we reduce the last equation to

$$\Delta F = q - T \Delta S.$$

And now it is clear how the crucial criteria expressed in equations (29) and (30) can be re-expressed in terms of F:

The criterion of a spontaneous change at constant T and P: $\Delta F < 0.$ (39)

The criterion of equilibrium in a system at constant T and P: $\Delta F = 0.$ (40)

No system is at equilibrium if it can undergo a change that reduces its capacity to do work. Only when a minimum free energy has been attained ($dF = 0$) is the system at equilibrium. The restriction to systems at constant temperature and pressure may seem seriously to limit the scope of this equilibrium criterion, but Lewis and Randall properly observe that

... if no reaction at constant temperature and pressure is thermodynamically possible, no reaction whatever can occur. For suppose that some spontaneous process could occur in such a way as to produce inequalities of temperature and pressure within the system or to produce a difference between the temperature and pressure of the system and the temperature and pressure of the environment; then this process could be followed by another obviously spontaneous process, consisting in the equalization of pressure and temperature. But these two processes together would be the equivalent of a spontaneous process occurring at constant temperature and pressure.

It is therefore a general criterion of equilibrium, with respect to *every possible change*, that the free energy remain unchanged in any infinitesimal process occurring at constant temperature and pressure.

Equation (37) tells us that

$$\Delta F = \Delta H - T \Delta S.$$

We see here how the direction of the spontaneous chemical reaction is

TABLE 3

ΔH	ΔS	ΔF
−	+	− reaction always spontaneous
+	−	+ reaction never spontaneous
−	−	? direction depends on the conditions
+	+	? direction depends on the conditions

controlled. Clearly, loss of heat content $(-\Delta H)$ and increase in entropy $(+\Delta S)$ both tend to produce $(-\Delta F)$ spontaneous reaction. Four possible situations are indicated in Table 3. At sufficiently low temperatures (minimizing the $T \Delta S$ term), exothermic reactions $(-\Delta H)$ will be spontaneous $(-\Delta F)$; at sufficiently high temperatures the $T \Delta S$ term must become dominant. A complex compound formed from its elements in an exothermic reaction will be stable at low temperatures even though, since it is a comparatively highly ordered structure, the ΔS term is negative. But, assuming constant pressure, at high temperatures this compound, like complex compounds generally, will become unstable as the $T \Delta S$ term assumes control.

As in the case of E and H, only *changes* in F are thermodynamically significant, and for convenience we may arbitrarily assign zero free energy to the elements in their standard states at 25°C. For these we say $F^0_{298} = 0$, and we can then calculate ΔF^0_f, the free energy of formation of one mole of any compound. For consider that $\Delta F^0_f = \Delta H^0_f - T \Delta S^0_f$. We have already shown that a standard heat of formation, ΔH^0_f, is determinable either directly, or indirectly with the aid of Hess's law. We have also shown how (from purely thermal data and the third principle of thermodynamics) we can attain, for all pure elements and compounds, values of S^0_{298}. Given these, any ΔS^0_f is easily found. And then, knowing both ΔS^0_f and ΔH^0_f, we easily find ΔF^0_f—the free energy of formation of any compound in its standard state at 25°C. Moreover, since F is a function of state, ΔF^0_f values can be added, subtracted, and manipulated in exactly the same fashion that ΔH terms are handled in calculations by means of Hess's law. Hence, even if the requisite ΔH^0_f and ΔS^0_f data for some particular compound are not available, we may still be able to determine ΔF^0_f for the compound, by an indirect calculation in the style of Hess's law. And then—just as we were able to calculate heats of reaction as soon as we were given heats of formation for the compounds involved— we can proceed here in exactly the same fashion to calculate ΔF^0_{298} for any reaction as soon as we know ΔF^0_f (presumed calculated for 298°K) for the compounds involved. For the completely general case we represent by n_J the number of moles of each reactant, J, consumed, and by n_K the number of moles of each product, K, formed. For the reaction, as written, we have then

$$\Delta F^0_{298} = \sum n_K \, \Delta F^0_{fK} - \sum n_J \, \Delta F^0_{fJ}.$$

The possibility of so determining ΔF^0_{298} is of immense importance, as we shall soon see.

The Clausius-Clapeyron Equation. To capitalize fully on the criterion of equilibrium constituted by $\Delta F = 0$, we must now embark on a brief excursion into the differential calculus. For any given change proceeding reversibly along any given path, the first principle assumes the form of equation (28):

$$dE = q_{\text{rev}} - w_{\text{max}}.$$

Noting that dS is defined in terms of q_{rev}, and stipulating that the only work possible is $P \, dV$ work, we write:

$$dE = T \, dS - P \, dV. \tag{41}$$

Although this equation has been derived for the special case of a reversible change, it is easily shown to hold generally.*

Our definition of H is

$$H = E + PV.$$

Differentiating, we have

$$dH = dE + P \, dV + V \, dP.$$

Substituting for dE then yields

$$dH = T \, dS - P \, dV + P \, dV + V \, dP,$$
$$dH = T \, dS + V \, dP. \tag{42}$$

Lastly, consider the definition of F:

$$F = H - TS.$$

Differentiation yields

$$dF = dH - T \, dS - S \, dT.$$

Substitution for dH then yields

$$dF = T \, dS + V \, dP - T \, dS - S \, dT,$$
$$dF = V \, dP - S \, dT. \tag{43}$$

---

* Suppose the change to be partially or wholly irreversible. The work recovered will be less than w_{max} and will be represented $(w_{\text{max}} - \alpha)$. But since, for a given change, dE is always the same, the heat term corresponding to $(w_{\text{max}} - \alpha)$ must be $(q_{\text{rev}} - \alpha)$. Thus even when the change is not reversible it will still be true that

$$dE = (q_{\text{rev}} - \alpha) - (w_{\text{max}} - \alpha) = q_{\text{rev}} - w_{\text{max}} = T \, dS - P \, dV.$$

All our subsequent derivations will take departure from this one equation.*

Suppose we have a given pure substance existing in two phases that are in equilibrium with each other (e.g., a solid in equilibrium with its melt, a liquid in equilibrium with its vapor, etc.). Since the two phases are in equilibrium it follows at once that the free energy per mole of the material in one phase, $\overline{F}_1$, must be equal to the free energy per mole of material in the second phase, $\overline{F}_2$.† Were this not so there would exist a nonzero ΔF, as a result of which material would transfer from one phase to the other, in a spontaneous change. But no such change is detectable in a system at equilibrium. Therefore

$$\overline{F}_1 = \overline{F}_2.$$

Now suppose a new equilibrium established at a temperature and pressure infinitesimally different from those before prevailing. The new state being again an equilibrium condition, the argument given above requires that the new free energies be equal. Therefore

$$\overline{F}_1 + d\overline{F}_1 = \overline{F}_2 + d\overline{F}_2.$$

Together, the last two equations require that

$$d\overline{F}_1 = d\overline{F}_2.$$

Substitution from equation (43) now yields

$$-\overline{S}_1 \, dT + \overline{V}_1 \, dP = -\overline{S}_2 \, dT + \overline{V}_2 \, dP,$$
$$(\overline{S}_2 - \overline{S}_1) \, dT = (\overline{V}_2 - \overline{V}_1) \, dP,$$
$$\Delta \overline{S} \, dT = \Delta \overline{V} \, dP.$$

With $\Delta \overline{F} = 0$ at equilibrium, equation (37) tells us that $\Delta \overline{S} = \Delta \overline{H}/T$. And, to be sure, the change of entropy is simply the heat involved in the reversible transfer of one mole of substance from one phase to the other, divided by the temperature at which the transfer takes place. Therefore

$$\Delta \overline{V} \, dP = \frac{\Delta \overline{H}}{T} \, dT. \tag{45}$$

This is the Clapeyron equation, a simple and rigorous relation of extreme generality that applies indifferently to vaporization, fusion, and sublimation, as well as to interconversions of allotropic forms like diamond and graphite, and so on. In terms of the changes in molar volume and heat content accompanying any phase transition, and given the temperature

---

* The corresponding equation in A is easily shown to be

$$dA = -P \, dV - S \, dT. \tag{44}$$

† The bar above the symbol will, throughout the remainder of these notes, signify the value of an extensive variable of state *per mole of material*.

and pressure corresponding to some one equilibrium condition for that transition, the Clapeyron equation permits calculation of the entire coordinated set of temperatures and pressures describing *all* equilibrium states for that transition. With condensed phases, ordinarily $\Delta \overline{H} \gg T \, \Delta \overline{V}$, and so we are led to expect what indeed we find: the slope dT/dP is very flat, i.e., quite large changes of equilibrium pressure are required to produce much change of equilibrium temperature.

Consider as an example the equilibrium between ice and water, which at one atmosphere pressure is established at 0°C. Measurement of the densities of ice and water under these conditions yields figures of 0.917 gm/ml and 1.000 gm/ml. For the conversion of ice to water the molar volume change is then

$$\Delta \overline{V} = \frac{18}{1.00} - \frac{18}{0.917} = 18 \left(1 - \frac{1}{0.917} \right) = 18(1 - 1.091) = -18(0.091) \text{ ml.}$$

To melt one mole of ice the following increase in heat content is required: $\Delta \overline{H} = (18)(80) \text{ cal} = (18)(80)(41.3) \text{ ml-atm.}$ The factor 41.3 converts calories to the energy unit ml-atm: with $\Delta \overline{V}$ expressed in milliliters, as it is, pressure will be expressed in atmospheres in the answer now obtained by substitution in equation (45):

$$-(18)(0.091) \, dP = \frac{(18)(80)(41.3)}{273} \, dT.$$

The cancellation of the 18 from this equation makes clear what may already have been guessed: ΔH and ΔV need only refer to the *same* quantity of material (e.g., one gram) and not necessarily to one mole. Note too that it makes no difference whether we express ΔH and ΔV for the melting of ice or for the freezing of water, but, if an answer with the correct sign is desired, it is essential that both do refer to the *same* direction of change.

Resolving the last equation, we have at last

$$\frac{dT}{dP} = - \frac{(273)(0.091)}{(80)(41.3)} = -0.0075°\text{K/atm.}$$

We have thus calculated the change of equilibrium temperature with pressure in the vicinity of 273°K.* Ice is *less* dense than water, so that by Le Chatelier's principle an increase in pressure should promote the melting of ice. Beyond that qualitative prediction, the above calculation tells us precisely how much the temperature must be lowered to compensate for the effect of the increase in pressure—that is, to maintain the equilibrium of

---

* Given the previously remarked flatness of the plot of T vs. P, even a pressure of 1000 atm does not carry us far enough from 273°K to put our calculations seriously in error. But at extreme pressures we can no longer simply substitute 273 for T in equation (45); instead we must treat T as a variable, so that the equation assumes the form $d \ln T/dP = \Delta V/\Delta H$.

ice and water under pressure. For a solid which, like most solids, is *more* dense than its melt, ΔV for the conversion of solid to liquid will have a positive sign and dT/dP will then be positive, i.e., increase of pressure will produce a *rise* of the melting point. Again the qualitative prediction of Le Chatelier's principle is confirmed, and *supplanted*, by a quantitative relation drawn from the Clapeyron equation. Conversely, given actual measurements of ΔV and dT/dP for some phase transition, we can calculate a ΔH value that may be difficult to measure directly (e.g., under conditions of extreme pressure).

When one of the two phases involved is a gas (e.g., as in vaporization and sublimation phenomena), we can recast the Clapeyron equation in a convenient approximate form. Assuming that the molar volume of the liquid is negligible compared with the molar volume of the gas, and assuming further that the gas can be approximated as ideal, we write

$$\Delta \overline{V} = \overline{V}_G - \overline{V}_L \doteq \overline{V}_G = \frac{RT}{P}.$$

Substitution in equation (45) now yields the Clausius-Clapeyron equation:

$$\frac{RT}{P} dP = \frac{\Delta \overline{H}}{T} dT.$$

With the understanding that this equation is always to refer to one mole of material, we now drop the bar from $\Delta \overline{H}$ and, after rearrangement, write:

$$\frac{dP}{P} = d \ln P = \frac{\Delta H}{RT^2} dT. \tag{46}$$

As a final approximation, consider ΔH to be invariant with temperature and integrate:

$$\int_{P_1}^{P_2} d \ln P = \frac{\Delta H}{R} \int_{T_1}^{T_2} \frac{dT}{T^2},$$

$$\ln \frac{P_2}{P_1} = - \frac{\Delta H}{R} \left(\frac{1}{T_2} - \frac{1}{T_1} \right). \tag{47}$$

Despite the several approximations involved, equations (46) and (47) apply very well to an immense number of measurements of vapor pressure over various liquids and solids. Plots of $\ln P$ vs. $1/T$ are generally quite satisfactorily rectilinear, and from the slope of these plots $(= -\Delta H/R)$ the heat of volatilization can be read off with surprising accuracy.

Colligative Properties. Turning now to the treatment of solutions, we require an expression descriptive or prescriptive of an ideal solution, in just the sense that the equation $PV = nRT$ defines for us an ideal gas. For solutions we find the needed expression in Raoult's law, $P = P^0 X$, where P^0 is the vapor pressure over the pure solvent at that temperature at which

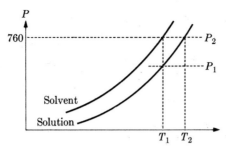

FIGURE 23

P is its vapor pressure over a solution in which its mole fraction is X. With the aid of the Clausius-Clapeyron equation we can now derive, for ideal solutions, all the colligative property laws ordinarily stated only as empirical regularities and/or justified by inadequate kinetic arguments. Our derivations will all assume that the heat of vaporization of a mole of solvent from the solution is adequately approximated as the heat required for the corresponding vaporization from the pure solvent. Can this assumption be defended? Eminently plausible for the very dilute solutions with which we shall be concerned, this assumption is actually no approximation at all; one can easily demonstrate that the heat terms *must* be equal for any solution that conforms to the standard of ideality set by Raoult's law.*

The boiling point elevation. Consider the state of a dilute solution of an involatile solute. As indicated in Fig. 23, at T_1 the solution doesn't boil

---

* Let $(\Delta H_{vap})_{soln}$ represent the heat of vaporization of a mole of solvent from the solution, and let ΔH_{vap} represent the molar heat of vaporization from the pure solvent. By equation (46) we can then write for the solution

$$\frac{d \ln P}{dT} = \frac{(\Delta H_{vap})_{soln}}{RT^2},$$ (a)

and for the solvent

$$\frac{d \ln P^0}{dT} = \frac{\Delta H_{vap}}{RT^2}.$$ (b)

We now stipulate that the solution obeys Raoult's law, $P = P^0 X$, which we write in logarithmic form as

$$\ln P = \ln P^0 + \ln X.$$

For any given solution (with X a constant) differentiation with respect to temperature yields

$$\frac{d \ln P}{dT} = \frac{d \ln P^0}{dT}.$$ (c)

Bearing in mind that Raoult's law compares solution and solvent at the *same* temperature, we at once conclude from equations (a), (b), and (c) that:

$$(\Delta H_{vap})_{soln} = \Delta H_{vap}.$$

because it has only the vapor pressure P_1. The solution does boil only as it reaches temperature T_2, at which point its vapor pressure, P_2, is that of the pure solvent at temperature T_1. Now Raoult's law, in the symbols of the present discussion, runs:

$$P_1 = P_2 X_{\text{solvent}},$$

whence

$$\ln \frac{P_2}{P_1} = \ln \frac{1}{X_{\text{solvent}}}.$$

Substitution in equation (47) then yields

$$\ln \frac{1}{X_{\text{solvent}}} = \ln \frac{1}{1 - X_{\text{solute}}} = -\frac{\Delta H_{\text{vap}}}{R}\left(\frac{1}{T_2} - \frac{1}{T_1}\right). \qquad (48)$$

Consider now that

$$\ln \frac{1}{1 - \beta} = \beta + \frac{\beta^2}{2} + \frac{\beta^3}{3} + \cdots$$

and when β is much less than 1 the first term of this series is all that counts. Therefore we can write for a very dilute solution that

$$X_{\text{solute}} = \frac{\Delta H_{\text{vap}}}{R}\left(\frac{T_2 - T_1}{T_2 T_1}\right).$$

If T_1 is the normal boiling point of the pure solvent, then the numerator $(T_2 - T_1)$ is the boiling point elevation, ΔT. Moreover, if, as already stipulated, the solution is very dilute, then T_2 will not be very different from T_1 and the term $T_2 T_1$ in the denominator can be approximated as $(T_1)^2$ or, if we call the normal boiling point T_B, simply as $(T_B)^2$. We then have

$$X_{\text{solute}} = \frac{\Delta H_{\text{vap}}}{R}\left(\frac{\Delta T}{T_B^2}\right).$$

Invoking for the last time the diluteness of the solution, we write

$$X_{\text{solute}} = \frac{\text{moles solute}}{\text{moles solute} + \text{moles solvent}} \doteq \frac{\text{moles solute}}{\text{moles solvent}}$$

$$= \frac{\text{moles solute}/1000 \text{ gm solvent}}{1000/M_{\text{solvent}}} = \frac{m M_{\text{solvent}}}{1000}.$$

Here m represents the molality of the solute, and M_{solvent} the molecular weight of the solvent. Substitution now gives

$$\frac{m M_{\text{solvent}}}{1000} = \frac{\Delta H_{\text{vap}} \Delta T}{R T_B^2},$$

$$\Delta T = \left[\frac{R T_B^2 M_{\text{solvent}}}{1000 \, \Delta H_{\text{vap}}}\right] m. \qquad (49)$$

TABLE 4

ELEVATION OF THE BOILING-POINT FOR SOME NONELECTROLYTIC SOLUTES

Solvent	Boiling-point at 1 atm, °K	ΔH_{vap} kcal/mole	Molecular elevation	
			calc.	obs.
Water	373.2	9.72	0.513	0.51
Acetone	329.3	7.28	1.72	1.72
Carbon tetrachloride	349.9	7.17	5.22	4.9
Chloroform	334.4	7.02	3.78	3.9
Ethyl alcohol	351.7	9.22	1.23	1.20
Methyl alcohol	337.9	8.43	0.86	0.84
Diethyl ether	307.6	6.61	2.11	2.16
Benzene	353.3	7.35	2.63	2.6

The bracketed term on the right contains only terms referring to the solvent, so for all ideal solutions in any one given solvent we can write

$$\Delta T = K_B m.$$

Despite the many approximations involved in its derivation, equation (49) is in excellent agreement with the results obtained with a variety of solvents as shown in Table 4.

The freezing point depression. The freezing point depression of a solution can be derived by an argument only slighty more complicated than that above. Instead of freezing at T_1, the freezing point of the pure solvent (Fig. 24), the solution freezes at T_2, the temperature at which its vapor pressure at last equals the vapor pressure of the solid solvent at the same temperature. *Will* the solution curve always intersect the curve of the solid solvent? Yes! By equation (46), the vapor pressure of the solid solvent falls off according to the equation

$$\frac{d \ln P_s}{dT} = \frac{\Delta H_{sub}}{RT^2},$$

where ΔH_{sub} is the molar heat of sublimation and P_s is the vapor pressure over the solid. For the solution,

$$\frac{d \ln P_n}{dT} = \frac{\Delta H_{vap}}{RT^2},$$

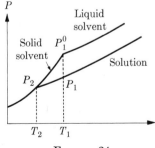

FIGURE 24

TABLE 5

DEPRESSION OF THE FREEZING POINT FOR SOME NONELECTROLYTIC
SOLUTES

Solvent	Freezing-point, °K	ΔH_{fus}, kcal/mole	Molecular depression	
			calc.	obs.
Water	273.2	1.436	1.86	1.86
Benzene	278.7	2.378	5.07	5.12
Naphthalene	353.4	4.565	6.97	6.9
Carbon tetrachloride	250.3	0.60	32	30
Chloroform	209.7	2.2	4.7	4.9
Ethylene dibromide	283.1	2.62	11.4	12.5
Acetic acid	289.8	2.80	3.6	3.9
Phenol	314.2	2.70	6.8	7.3

where ΔH_{vap} is the molar heat of vaporization and P_n is the vapor pressure of the solution. Now observe that Hess's law requires that

$$\Delta H_{sub} = \Delta H_{vap} + \Delta H_{fus},$$

where ΔH_{fus} represents the heat of fusion. But this means that necessarily $\Delta H_{sub} > \Delta H_{vap}$, whence it also follows that

$$\frac{d \ln P_s}{dT} > \frac{d \ln P_n}{dT}.$$

Beginning higher up, at the normal freezing point, the vapor pressure curve of the pure solid falls off more steeply than the vapor pressure curve of the solution, so that the two are bound to intersect as shown.

Now to the derivation. For the vapor pressure of the solution we write, as before,

$$\ln \frac{P_2}{P_1} = -\frac{\Delta H_{vap}}{R}\left(\frac{1}{T_2} - \frac{1}{T_1}\right).$$

Over the pure solid form of the solvent, we have

$$\ln \frac{P_2}{P_1^0} = -\frac{\Delta H_{sub}}{R}\left(\frac{1}{T_2} - \frac{1}{T_1}\right).$$

Subtracting the second equation from the first yields

$$\ln \frac{P_2}{P_1} - \ln \frac{P_2}{P_1^0} = \frac{(\Delta H_{sub} - \Delta H_{vap})}{R}\left(\frac{1}{T_2} - \frac{1}{T_1}\right),$$

whence

$$\ln \frac{P_1^0}{P_1} = \frac{\Delta H_{fus}}{R}\left(\frac{1}{T_2} - \frac{1}{T_1}\right).$$

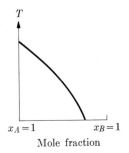

FIG. 25. As is: Melting point as a function of composition.
Rotated 90°: Solubility as a function of temperature.

For the ideal solution defined by Raoult's law it then follows that

$$\ln \frac{1}{X_{\text{solvent}}} = \frac{\Delta H_{\text{fus}}}{R} \left(\frac{1}{T_2} - \frac{1}{T_1} \right). \tag{50}$$

From here a development identical with that which carried us from equation (48) to equation (49) here produces as the freezing point depression relation

$$\Delta T = \left[\frac{RT_F^2 M_{\text{solvent}}}{1000 \, \Delta H_{\text{fus}}} \right] m = K_F m. \tag{51}$$

Again a good agreement with experimental values is found, as shown in Table 5.

Solubility: a colligative property? From freezing point depressions to solubilities is but a short step. Says Caldin:

If the pure solvent separates when a solution is cooled we speak of the freezing point at a given concentration; if the pure solute separates, we commonly . . . speak of the solubility at a given temperature; but thermodynamically the two equilibria are very similar, the only difference being that in the first the solid phase consists of the constituent in excess, and in the second it consists of the other constituent.

In Fig. 25 the curve shows the temperature at which solid *A* begins to separate from an *A-B* solution. This curve we may hold to represent the depression of the freezing point of *A* produced by addition of *B* or, alternatively, the solubility of solid *A* in *B*. It is simply a matter of whether we choose to regard temperature as a function of concentration or, alternatively, concentration as a function of temperature.

Since we are considering solubilities rather than freezing point depressions, we are concerned with more concentrated solutions for which the approximations of great dilution will not serve. We must begin, then, not with equation (51), but rather with equation (50). Note, however, that

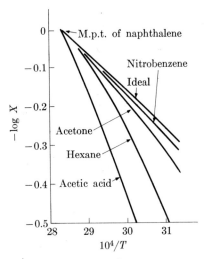

FIG. 26. Temperature dependence of the solubility of naphthalene in various solvents.

what we formerly took to be the solvent (i.e., the material that separates out as a pure solid phase) will now be called the solute (i.e., the material that dissolves to form a saturated solution), and that, correspondingly, T_1, which was formerly called the freezing point of the pure solvent, will now be called the melting point (T_M) of the pure solute. These changes are made explicit by rewriting equation (50) as follows:

$$\ln X_{\text{solute}} = -\frac{\Delta H_{\text{fus}}}{R}\left(\frac{1}{T_2} - \frac{1}{T_M}\right). \tag{52}$$

We can then calculate solubility as a function of temperature (T_2) at all temperatures up to the melting point. Equation (52) suggests, surprisingly enough, that the solubility of any given substance is the same (in terms of mole fraction) in all solvents with which it forms ideal solutions. The powerful solvation effects accompanying the solution of electrolytes disqualifies these solutions as ideal. But that the prediction of equation (52) is sometimes a good approximation can be seen from Fig. 26, which shows the solubility of naphthalene in various solvents. Note that for some of these the plot of log X vs. $1/T$ is an excellent approximation to the predicted straight line. Note too the predictable convergence of all curves as the mole fraction of naphthalene approaches 1 (in which case, of course, the left side of the equation (52) goes to zero, so that $T_2 = T_M$).

Recognition of the relation between *freezing point depression* and the solubility of *solids* suggests the existence of an analogous relation between *boiling point elevation* and the solubility of *gases*. Review the chain of argument by which we passed from the freezing point depression relation,

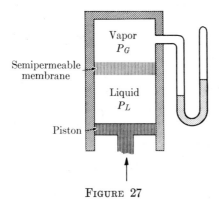

FIGURE 27

expressed in equation (50), to the solubility relation expressed in equation (52). Setting out now from equation (48), precisely the same line of argument brings us to the following relation expressing the variation with temperature of the solubility of a gas maintained at *constant pressure:*

$$\ln X_{\text{solute}} = \frac{\Delta H_{\text{vap}}}{R} \left(\frac{1}{T_2} - \frac{1}{T_B} \right).$$

If one atmosphere is to be the gas pressure maintained, T_B is the normal boiling point of the pure liquefied gas, but if some other constant pressure is used we simply substitute for T_B whatever *is* the boiling point of the pure liquefied gas under *that* pressure. Assume now that ΔH_{vap}, the molar heat of vaporization of the pure liquefied gas, reasonably approximates its heat of vaporization from solution. The last equation then indicates that, as in the case of solids, the solubility of a gas (expressed as a mole fraction) should be the same in all solvents with which it forms ideal solutions. The last equation, lacking the minus sign of equation (52), allows us to calculate, for a given rise of temperature, by just how much the solubility of the gas is *diminished* (not increased, as is the case for solids in ideal solutions).

Osmotic pressure. We come now to the last of the familiar colligative properties. Here we begin by asking about the (small) change in the vapor pressure of a pure liquid produced by change in the total pressure to which the liquid is subject. Imagine that there exists for any given liquid a membrane which behaves towards it as does a sintered glass disk towards mercury—that is, passing vapor but holding back liquid. With a piston we then apply to the liquid some pressure P_L and observe the effect on the vapor pressure P_G. Imagine that, having established equilibrium at some one pressure P_L, we infinitesimally increase that pressure and establish a new equilibrium *at the same temperature.* For the first condition of equilibrium, we have

$$\overline{F}_L - \overline{F}_G = \Delta \overline{F} = 0 \qquad \text{or} \qquad \overline{F}_L = \overline{F}_G.$$

For the second state of equilibrium, we have

$$(\overline{F}_L + d\overline{F}_L) - (\overline{F}_G + d\overline{F}_G) = \Delta\overline{F} = 0,$$

whence it follows that $d\overline{F}_L = d\overline{F}_G$.

At constant temperature $dT \equiv 0$, and equation (43) simplifies to

$$dF = V\,dP - S\,dT = V\,dP.$$

Combining the last two equations, we have then

$$\overline{V}_L\,dP_L = \overline{V}_G\,dP_G.$$

Subscripts are required to differentiate the pressure terms, for in an osmotic system the pressure on the two sides of the membrane will differ. Observe that since $\overline{V}_G$ and $\overline{V}_L$ are always finite and positive, increase in the pressure imposed on a liquid always increases its vapor pressure; but observe also that since $\overline{V}_G \gg \overline{V}_L$, moderate changes in the pressure imposed on the liquid produce no directly detectable change in its vapor pressure.

Now at a given temperature a solution *always* has a vapor pressure lower than that of the corresponding pure solvent, and we can regard, and calculate, osmotic pressure as the extra pressure that must be exerted on a solution in order that its vapor pressure shall equal that of the pure solvent. Only then will the solution be in equilibrium with the pure solvent on the other side of the semipermeable membrane. To apply the last equation to a liquid phase consisting of solution rather than pure solvent, we will assume that the volume occupied by one mole of solvent in the solution is the same as that occupied by one mole of pure solvent, $\overline{V}_L$— and this is an excellent approximation for dilute solutions. We further simplify by supposing the solution essentially incompressible, so that for a given solvent at a given temperature, $\overline{V}_L$ can be taken as a constant. We assume, finally, that the solvent vapor behaves like an ideal gas, so that the last equation can be rewritten as

$$\overline{V}_L\,dP_L = \frac{RT}{P_G}\,dP_G.$$

Given the foregoing assumptions, this equation is easily integrated as soon as we establish appropriate limits. Let us take as the lower limit that in which no extra pressure is exerted on the liquid phase, which has then simply the vapor pressure, P, appropriate to its concentration and temperature. Let us take as the upper limit that in which the additional (osmotic) pressure π, applied to the liquid phase, increases its vapor pressure to equal P^0, the vapor pressure of the pure solvent at the same temperature. We have then

$$\overline{V}_L \int_0^{\pi} dP_L = RT \int_P^{P^0} \frac{dP_G}{P_G},$$

$$\overline{V}_L \pi = RT \ln \frac{P^0}{P}. \tag{53}$$

Stipulating ideality of the solution, we now introduce Raoult's law, and obtain

$$\pi = \frac{RT}{\overline{V}_L} \ln \frac{1}{X_{\text{solvent}}}.$$

The same approximations used twice before for dilute solutions now yield

$$\pi = \frac{RT}{\overline{V}_L} X_{\text{solute}}.$$

For dilute solutions this can also be written as

$$\pi = \frac{RT}{\overline{V}_L} \frac{\text{moles solute}}{\text{moles solvent}}.$$

Observe that $\overline{V}_L$ is the volume of one mole of solvent in the solution, so that ($\overline{V}_L$·moles solvent) is simply the total volume of the solvent present —or, in dilute solution, the total volume V of the solution. Representing by n the moles of solute present, we then arrive at van't Hoff's osmotic pressure formula:

$$\pi V = nRT. \tag{54}$$

Equilibrium State and Equilibrium Constant. We have already seen that, setting out from equation (43), *at constant temperature* the variation with pressure of the free energy of a mole of the substance J is given by the equation $d\overline{F}_J = \overline{V}_J dP_J$. If the substance is a *perfect gas*, we then have

$$d\overline{F}_J = RT \frac{dP_J}{P_J}.$$

For integration, let us take the lower limit to be that in which the gas stands at a pressure of one atmosphere, and has, therefore, its standard free energy, $\overline{F}_J^0$. As the upper limit take the free energy $\overline{F}_J$ corresponding to any other pressure, P_J. Then one writes

$$\int_{\overline{F}_J^0}^{\overline{F}_J} d\overline{F}_J = RT \int_1^{P_J} \frac{dP_J}{P_J},$$

$$\overline{F}_J - \overline{F}_J^0 = RT \ln P_J. \tag{55}$$

To make this equation apply to any number of moles, n_J, of the ideal gas, we write

$$F_J = n_J \overline{F}_J = n_J \overline{F}_J^0 + n_J RT \ln P_J.$$

For the general case of a reaction involving ideal gases we represent by n_J the number of moles of each reactant, J, consumed; and by n_K the number of moles of each product, K, formed. For the reaction, as written, we then have

$$\Delta F = \sum n_K \overline{F}_K - \sum n_J \overline{F}_J.$$

Consider the case of a reaction of the form $gG + hH = lL + mM$. For this reaction we can write

$$\Delta F = l\overline{F}_L + m\overline{F}_M - g\overline{F}_G - h\overline{F}_H.$$

Now Dalton's law indicates that, to a good degree of approximation, in a mixture of real gases each is as a vacuum to the other(s). And certainly in a mixture of ideal gases we are justified in conceiving each as wholly independent of the presence of the others. The free energy of a mixture of ideal gases will then be simply the sum of the free energies of the component gases, each exerting its own partial pressure P_J. *For ideal gases* in a reaction mixture we can then substitute as follows:

$$\Delta F = [l\overline{F}_L^0 + m\overline{F}_M^0 - g\overline{F}_G^0 - h\overline{F}_H^0]$$
$$+ RT[l \ln P_L + m \ln P_M - g \ln P_G - h \ln P_H],$$

$$\Delta F = \Delta F^0 + RT \ln \frac{(P_L)^l (P_M)^m}{(P_G)^g (P_H)^h}.$$

Observe that the pressure function has precisely the *form* of the equilibrium constant for the reaction. Now let us suppose that the reaction has proceeded to equilibrium. At this point $\Delta F = 0$, and the pressures of the gases will be such that the pressure function takes on the *value* of the equilibrium constant, with partial pressures expressed in atmospheres. Thus:

$$0 = \Delta F^0 + RT \ln K_P \quad \text{or} \quad \ln K_P = -\frac{\Delta F^0}{RT}.$$

This surprisingly simple relation has so far been obtained only for the case of reactions involving strictly hypothetical ideal gases. Can it be generalized? Indeed it can, and easily! We find that a relation of the form of equation (55) can be written for *any* substance J in terms of the "activity," a_J, of that substance. Thus

$$\overline{F}_J = \overline{F}_J^0 + RT \ln a_J. \tag{56}$$

We can now set out from equation (56), as formerly we did from equation (55), and so obtain—now with *no* restriction to ideal gases—a relation just like the above save that the equilibrium constant, K_a, is now expressed in terms of activities. The activity of a substance is a function of its concentration, and sometimes—due to strong molecular interactions we could wholly ignore when dealing with hypothetical ideal gases—a very complicated function of concentration. By and large, however, with change in concentration the activity will at least change in the same direction; and often the activity is nothing but a "corrected concentration" obtained by multiplying the actual concentration by a suitable numerical coefficient derived from experiment or from (nonthermodynamic) treatment of the molecular interactions. Moreover, in systems constituted of mixtures of real gases at reasonably low pressures, and real solutions at reasonable dilutions, these numerical coefficients approach 1 as a limit, in which case $a = P$ and $a = X$ respectively. Most equilibrium studies have been made on what have proved to be just such "reasonable" systems, and we thus find that in the great majority of cases we can, with no major loss of accuracy, replace activities by more familiar partial pressure and mole fraction terms.

Provided that we take care to select the appropriate terms, and units, we find that for *any* reaction we can write

$$\Delta F = \Delta F^0 + RT \ln Z, \qquad (57)$$

where Z is some concentration function having the *form* of the equilibrium constant for the reaction concerned. And then, for *any* reaction at equilibrium, one has

$$-\Delta F^0 = RT \ln K. \qquad (58)$$

Ordinarily students of chemistry are first conducted to the equilibrium constant expression by way of not wholly satisfactory kinetic arguments. But in equations (57) and (58) we see the emergence of precisely the same expression from a more adequate thermodynamic argument that depends on no hypotheses about the mechanisms of chemical reactions and makes no reference whatever to kinetics. Moreover, the thermodynamic argument shows clearly how it is that, at any given temperature, K must be constant for all possible equilibrium mixtures. For consider that at any fixed temperature K is determined by the value of ΔF^0 for the reaction. With changes of concentration ΔF varies continuously (and reaches zero at equilibrium), but ΔF^0 is a difference of free energies of products and reactants *in their standard states.* Hence, unlike ΔF, ΔF^0 is *not* a function of concentration, and consequently $K = \exp(-\Delta F^0/RT)$ is also a constant independent of concentration.*

---

* In equation (56), as distinct from (55), $\overline{F}_J^0$ is likely to vary with the medium (e.g., the solvent) in which J finds itself, due to the variation of molecular interactions from one medium to another. But in any *given* medium each $\overline{F}_J^0$ term remains defined for some particular *standard* condition, and thus is totally independent of variation in *actual* concentration. In that medium ΔF^0 and K are then, as before, totally independent of concentration.

Our criterion of spontaneous reaction is $\Delta F < 0$; our criterion of equilibrium is $\Delta F = 0$. What if $\Delta F^0 = 0$? Then that mixture of all the reactants and all the products in which each is present at unit activity will be an equilibrium mixture—in which case, of course, $K = 1$, just as is required by equation (58). If $\Delta F^0 < 0$, then such a mixture is *not* at equilibrium, and equilibrium will be attained only when, with consumption of reactants and generation of products, the reaction has proceeded to the right. But when $\Delta F^0 < 0$ then $-\Delta F^0 > 0$ and $K > 1$, which is simply another way of saying that equilibrium lies to the right. The greater the margin by which $\Delta F^0 < 0$, the larger will be K and, in the reaction as written, the further to the right will lie the equilibrium state. If, on the other hand, $\Delta F^0 > 0$, then $K < 1$, which means that the reaction does *not* proceed spontaneously, and that the condition of equilibrium lies to the left.

The familiar expression for the equilibrium constant thus derives from a less familiar but much deeper-going criterion of equilibrium. Indeed, using the criterion $\Delta F = 0$, we become competent to establish the condition of equilibrium even when we can formulate no expression for the equilibrium constant in the usual sense. Consider, for example, the conversion of graphite to diamond: is it possible even in principle? To reach a decision we must determine ΔF^0 for the reaction, and this we can determine from accessible values of ΔS^0 and ΔH^0:

Heat capacity data yield for diamond $S^0_{298} = 0.58$ cal/mole·°K

Heat capacity data yield for graphite $S^0_{298} = 1.37$ cal/mole·°K

For C (graphite) $= C$ (diamond): $\Delta S^0_{298} = -0.79$ cal/mole·°K

On combustion: C (graph) $+ O_2 = CO_2$ $\Delta H^0_{298} = -94.03$ kcal

On combustion: C (diam) $+ O_2 = CO_2$ $\Delta H^0_{298} = -94.48$ kcal

For C (graphite) $= C$ (diamond): $\Delta H^0_{298} = +450$ cal/mole

Substituting now in equation (37), we find

$$\Delta F^0_{298} = \Delta H^0_{298} - T\,\Delta S^0_{298} = 450 - 298(-0.79) = +685 \text{ cal/mole}.$$

At room temperature the conversion of graphite to diamond under standard (1 atm pressure) conditions entails an increase in free energy. The spontaneous process is then the *inverse* conversion, i.e., of diamond into graphite, and under ordinary conditions diamond is a thermodynamically *unstable* species that exists only because the *rate* of its conversion to graphite is so slow.

The densities of diamond (3.5 gm/ml) and graphite (2.25 gm/ml) differ rather markedly:

For diamond: gm-atomic volume $= 12/3.5\ \ = 3.4$ ml/gm-atom

For graphite: gm-atomic volume $= 12/2.25 = 5.3$ ml/gm-atom

For C (graphite) $= C$ (diamond): $\Delta V_{298} = -1.9$ ml/gm-atom

The conversion is accompanied by a substantial decrease in volume, and we may then hope to favor the conversion of graphite to diamond by an increase of pressure. How much pressure will be needed to shift the balance of stability in favor of diamond? From equation (43) we have already concluded that at constant temperature

$$dF = V \, dP.$$

Using the subscripts D and G for diamond and graphite respectively, we write

$$dF_D = V_D \, dP,$$
$$dF_G = V_G \, dP,$$

whence

$$dF_D - dF_G = d(F_D - F_G) = (V_D - V_G) \, dP,$$

or

$$d \, \Delta F = \Delta V \, dP.$$

Assuming ΔV constant over the pressure range concerned, we can integrate. For the lower limit we take the standard pressure of one atmosphere, to which corresponds the value $\Delta F^0_{298} = 685$ cal, or $685(41.3) = 28{,}300$ ml-atm. For the upper limit we take that pressure P_{298} at which $\Delta F_{298} = 0$—that is, the condition under which diamond and graphite will be in equilibrium with each other.

$$\int_{28{,}300}^{0} d \, \Delta F = -1.9 \int_{1}^{P_{298}} dP,$$
$$0 - 28{,}300 = -1.9(P_{298} - 1),$$
$$P_{298} = 15{,}000 \text{ atm.}$$

At 25°C diamond and graphite would be in equilibrium at a pressure of 15,000 atm. At higher pressures graphite is thermodynamically unstable, and a conversion into diamond is possible in principle, although unattainable in practice because the rate of conversion is undetectably slow. Since at room temperature no equilibrium ever *is* attained, there remains room for skepticism that we *have* correctly determined what *would* be the equilibrium condition. But—given this specification of equilibrium state, and known values of ΔH and ΔV—the Clapeyron equation permits us to compute that pressure at which graphite and diamond will be in equilibrium at any other temperature. We may then determine that at 1500°K the equilibrium pressure is of the order of 50,000 atm, and here the detectable production of diamond from graphite at higher pressures testifies to the soundness of our calculation of the equilibrium state of the system.

The Galvanic Cell. Unlike any system so far considered, the galvanic cell is a device that can furnish net (electrical) work in excess of $P \, dV$ work. If a pair of half-cells, each containing some particular mixture of components, constitute a battery that furnishes a difference of potential of $\mathfrak{E}$ volts, then, per unit of reaction, we can write

$$\text{Net work} = \text{volts} \times \text{coulombs},$$

$$-\Delta F = \mathfrak{E} \cdot n\mathfrak{F} , \qquad (59)$$

where $\mathfrak{F}$ represents the faraday and n the number of faradays conveyed per unit of reaction. For a pair of half-cells in which all components are present in their standard states and concentrations, we write, similarly,

$$-\Delta F^0 = \mathfrak{E}^0 \cdot n\mathfrak{F},$$

where $\mathfrak{E}^0$ is the difference of potential between the *standard half-cells*. Substituting in equation (57), we find

$$n\mathfrak{F}\mathfrak{E} = n\mathfrak{F}\mathfrak{E}^0 - RT \ln Z,$$

or

$$\mathfrak{E} = \mathfrak{E}^0 - \frac{2.3 RT}{n\mathfrak{F}} \log Z. \qquad (60)$$

At equilibrium $\mathfrak{E}$, like ΔF, must become zero, and Z then assumes the value of the equilibrium constant K, so that

$$\log K = \frac{n\mathfrak{F}}{2.3 RT} \mathfrak{E}^0 = \underset{\underset{\text{At } 298^{\circ}\text{K}}{\uparrow}}{\frac{n}{0.059}} \mathfrak{E}^0.$$

Recall that $\mathfrak{E}^0$ is a *difference* of potential between two *standard* half-cells. The last equation then teaches us how—from readily available tabulations of standard half-cell potentials, $\mathcal{E}^0$—we can at once calculate the equilibrium constant for any redox reaction (in which, of course, all the components of two half-cells will, at equilibrium, occur together in a single vessel).*

Measurements of the difference of potential, $\mathfrak{E}$, delivered by a galvanic cell can often be carried out (with a potentiometer) under conditions of almost perfect reversibility. In favorable cases the difference of potential

---

* Those already familiar with the Nernst equation will recognize that it is easily derivable from equation (60). Imagine a half-cell in which a atoms, molecules, or ions of some material in its reduced form (Red) pass over into b atoms, molecules, or ions of that material in its oxidized form (Ox), with the release of n electrons, according to the reaction a Red $= b$ Ox $+ n\epsilon$. Let this half-cell be coupled with a standard hydrogen half-cell in which the reaction is $\frac{1}{2}H_2 = H^+ + \epsilon$, and for which, by definition, $\mathcal{E} = \mathcal{E}^0 = 0$ when the pressure of gaseous hydrogen is 1 atm and the concentration (better, activity) of hydrogen ion is also 1. Substitution in equation (60) then yields for the first half-cell the following fundamental (Nernst) relation of electrochemistry:

$$\mathcal{E} = \mathcal{E}^0 - \frac{2.3 RT}{n\mathfrak{F}} \log \frac{(Ox)^b}{(Red)^a} .$$

is easily determined with an uncertainty of less than ± 0.001 volt. From this difference of potential $-\Delta F$ can then be calculated, through equation (59), with an uncertainty of less than ± 23 cal/mole for a reaction in which $n = 1$. Considering that ΔF values can run to many tens of *kilo*calories per mole of reaction, a measurement of cell potential may offer an excellent, and often the very best available, determination of ΔF. And we can push on somewhat further. By measuring also the variation with temperature of the voltage delivered by the cell, we obtain good values for ΔH and ΔS of the reaction involved. This electrochemical determination of ΔS offers us a golden opportunity for a cross-check of electrochemical data with purely thermal data and the third principle of thermodynamics. Let us see how this possibility materializes.

If we impose a condition of *constant pressure*, equation (43) is reduced to

$$dF = -S \, dT.$$

Suppose we represent by the subscript "reac" all the reactants *collectively*, and by the subscript "prod" all the products *collectively*. For the temperature dependence of the free energies of these, we then have

$$dF_{\text{reac}} = -S_{\text{reac}} \, dT,$$
$$dF_{\text{prod}} = -S_{\text{prod}} \, dT.$$

Subtraction of the first equation from the second yields

$$dF_{\text{prod}} - dF_{\text{reac}} = d(F_{\text{prod}} - F_{\text{reac}}) = -(S_{\text{prod}} - S_{\text{reac}}) \, dT,$$
$$\frac{d(\Delta F)}{dT} = -\Delta S.$$

But from equation (37) we already know that

$$\Delta F = \Delta H - T \, \Delta S.$$

Substituting in this, we arrive at once at the Gibbs-Helmholtz equation:

$$\Delta F = \Delta H + T \, \frac{d(\Delta F)}{dT} \, . \tag{61}$$

The application of this equation to work with galvanic cells is not far to seek, for we can now substitute directly from equation (59) to find

$$-n\mathfrak{F}\mathfrak{E} = \Delta H - Tn\mathfrak{F}\left(\frac{d\mathfrak{E}}{dT}\right).$$

Thus from measurements of cell potential, and the coefficient of its variation with temperature at *constant pressure* $(d\mathfrak{E}/dT)$, we find

$$\Delta H = n\mathfrak{F}\left[T\left(\frac{d\mathfrak{E}}{dT}\right) - \mathfrak{E}\right].$$

But now that we have both ΔF and ΔH in terms of $\mathfrak{E}$ and $(d\mathfrak{E}/dT)$, we can at once establish a value for ΔS in the same terms. Turning again to equation (37), we find

$$\Delta S = \frac{\Delta H - \Delta F}{T} = \frac{n\mathfrak{F}T\left(\dfrac{d\mathfrak{E}}{dT}\right) - n\mathfrak{F}\mathfrak{E} + n\mathfrak{F}\mathfrak{E}}{T} = n\mathfrak{F}\left(\frac{d\mathfrak{E}}{dT}\right).$$

If standard half-cells are involved, all the $\mathfrak{E}$ and $d\mathfrak{E}/dT$ terms become $\mathfrak{E}^0$ and $d\mathfrak{E}^0/dT$ terms, and if we work with these half-cells at 298°K then the values calculated as above will be those of ΔF^0_{298}, ΔH^0_{298}, and ΔS^0_{298} for the reaction occurring in the cell. Now we saw much earlier (pages 50–51) that ΔS^0_{298} can also be determined from such purely *thermal* data as heat capacities, heats of fusion and vaporization, and the like—together with the third principle of thermodynamics. This thermal value for ΔS^0_{298} can then be compared with the above *completely* independent determination of ΔS^0_{298} from purely *electrical* data and with *no* reference to the third principle. This cross-check is an exceedingly searching test: in the electrical method $d\mathfrak{E}^0/dT$ is not nearly as well established as $\mathfrak{E}^0_{298}$; in the thermal method the entire accumulated error in measurements and calculations extending all the way back to 0°K will show up in the value of ΔS^0_{298}, the accuracy of which may often be still further weakened by the fact that it is determined only as a comparatively small difference between much larger figures. All these difficulties notwithstanding, the agreement of the two values of ΔS^0_{298} is generally good, and for some reactions almost unbelievably good. Consider the following system:

$$\text{Ag (s), AgCl (s)} | \text{HCl (aq, 1 m)} | \text{Cl}_2 \text{ (g, 1 atm), (Pt–Ir)}.$$

When charge is drawn from this galvanic cell the net reaction is

$$\text{Ag (s)} + \tfrac{1}{2}\text{Cl}_2 \text{ (g)} = \text{AgCl (s)}.$$

In the vicinity of 298°K the measured variation with temperature of the cell potential is -0.000595 volt/°K. We can then conclude that for the net reaction

$$\Delta S^0_{298} = n\mathfrak{F}\frac{d\mathfrak{E}^0}{dT} = (1)(96500)(0.000595) = 57.4 \text{ joules/°K},$$

or

$$13.73 \pm 0.10 \text{ cal/°K}.$$

From the third principle and from purely thermal data for the three materials *individually*, we obtain for the same reaction $\Delta S^0_{298} = 13.85 \pm 0.25$ cal/°K. Agreement such as this gives ample ground for confidence in our experimental methods and in our application of the third principle.

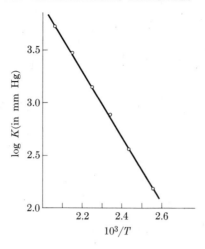

FIG. 28. Variation with temperature of the equilibrium constant for the vapor phase dissociation of acetic acid dimer, $(CH_3COOH)_2 = 2CH_3COOH$. [Data of Johnson and Nash, *J. Am. Chem. Soc.* **72**, 547 (1950).]

Temperature Dependence of the Equilibrium Constant. We know well that, although invariant at constant temperature, the equilibrium constant K *does* change with changing temperature. But this is precisely what the thermodynamic argument teaches us to expect. By equation (37),

$$\Delta F^0 = \Delta H^0 - T \Delta S^0,$$

whence it is evident that ΔF^0 is a function of temperature. This being so, it follows necessarily that K is also a function of temperature. What function? Combining the last equation with equation (58), we have

$$\ln K = \frac{-\Delta F^0}{RT} = \frac{-\Delta H^0 + T \Delta S^0}{RT} = \frac{-\Delta H^0}{RT} + \frac{\Delta S^0}{R}.$$

Suppose now that we compare with each other the values of K over a temperature span in which ΔH^0 is constant. Referring to equation (11), we see that the constancy of ΔH^0 requires that ΔC_P be negligibly small—under which condition equation (27) tells us that ΔS^0 must also be constant. We then write

$$\ln K_2 = \frac{-\Delta H^0}{RT_2} + \frac{\Delta S^0}{R}, \qquad \ln K_1 = \frac{-\Delta H^0}{RT_1} + \frac{\Delta S^0}{R}.$$

Subtracting the second equation from the first, we find

$$\ln \frac{K_2}{K_1} = 2.303 \log \frac{K_2}{K_1} = -\frac{\Delta H^0}{R} \left(\frac{1}{T_2} - \frac{1}{T_1} \right). \tag{62}$$

This is van't Hoff's law, and it applies excellently to a great many systems, one of which is represented in Fig. 28.

Observe that deductions drawn from equation (62) are in perfect agreement with the qualitative predictions of Le Chatelier's principle. Consider that $T_2 > T_1$. For an endothermic reaction $\Delta H > 0$, $-\Delta H/R < 0$, the right side of the last equation is positive, and $K_2 > K_1$. That is, the rise of temperature favors the endothermic reaction, which has a greater equilibrium constant at the higher temperature. For an exothermic reaction, on the other hand, $\Delta H < 0$, $-\Delta H/R > 0$, the right side of the last equation is negative, and $K_2 < K_1$. That is, an exothermic reaction is favored with a greater equilibrium constant at the lower temperature. But beyond such qualitative predictions, which are the most that Le Chatelier's principle can furnish, equation (62) invests us with the power actually to calculate the change of equilibrium constant with temperature.

Observe that on a plot of $\log K$ vs. $1/T$ the slope of the line is $-\Delta H/2.3R$. If ΔH is constant over the temperature range concerned, the slope of the line is constant; i.e., the line is straight, as in Fig. 28. Given the value of K at several temperatures we can then read off from the plot a value of ΔH that can be compared with (or stand in lieu of) values determined by direct calorimetry. If ΔH is not constant, this will manifest itself in a curvature of the plot of $\log K$ vs. $1/T$. We can still draw the tangent at a point, and so determine ΔH for that temperature, but such a curvature signalizes the breakdown of the assumption on which the derivation of (62) was based. We can then no longer depend on that equation for our calculation of the change in equilibrium constant over great ranges of temperature. However, we can easily derive an equation on which we can rely even in these circumstances.

Observe that of the terms appearing in equation (58) three vary with temperature: K, ΔF^0, and T itself. Differentiating with respect to T, we have then

$$-\frac{d\,\Delta F^0}{dT} = R \ln K + RT \frac{d \ln K}{dT}.$$

But now we can substitute for $d\,\Delta F^0/dT$ from the Gibbs-Helmholtz relation, our equation (61), and so obtain

$$\frac{\Delta H^0 - \Delta F^0}{T} = R \ln K + RT \frac{d \ln K}{dT}.$$

Substituting now for ΔF^0, again from equation (58), we find

$$\frac{\Delta H^0 + RT \ln K}{T} = R \ln K + RT \frac{d \ln K}{dT},$$

$$\frac{\Delta H^0}{T} + R \ln K = R \ln K + RT \frac{d \ln K}{dT},$$

TABLE 6

	ΔH^0, kcal/mole	S^0_{298}, cal/mole·°K	C_P, cal/mole·°K
N_2 (g)	—	45.76	6.96
H_2 (g)	—	31.21	6.89
NH_3 (g)	11.04	46.01	8.52

so that, finally, we have

$$\frac{d \ln K}{dT} = \frac{\Delta H^0}{RT^2}. \tag{63}$$

When ΔH^0 is constant, this expression integrates to equation (62). But should ΔH^0 prove inconstant, we will express it as a function of temperature—in terms of ΔC_P, as indicated in equation (12)—and substitute that function in equation (63). Integration then yields a more complex expression from which, however, we can read off the variation of K with temperature precisely as we do from equation (62) when ΔH is constant.

We saw earlier that, given data on ΔS^0_{298} and ΔH^0_{298}, we can calculate ΔF^0_{298} for any reaction. We see now that, given such a value for ΔF^0_{298}, equation (58) permits us to calculate the equilibrium constant of the reaction at 25°C. We see further that—given these data, the value of K, and data on the heat capacities of the materials concerned—equation (62) or (63) will permit the calculation of the equilibrium constant at any temperature. *Given purely thermal data, we can calculate the equilibrium constant of any reaction at any temperature—even though the reaction may never have been achieved under any circumstances.* It is this kind of calculation that sustains and guides what might otherwise seem forlorn endeavors to encompass what men have previously striven in vain to do. Thus, for example, thermodynamic considerations brought Nernst and Haber to an ammonia synthesis that had previously eluded the best efforts of such highly competent investigators as Ramsay and Le Chatelier. This first major technologic exploitation of thermodynamics perhaps remains even today, half a century later, that which most profoundly affects mankind. Let us then examine the thermodynamics of the Haber process, using modern data throughout.

Never before Haber had anyone observed the reaction

$$\tfrac{1}{2}N_2 + \tfrac{3}{2}H_2 \rightarrow NH_3.$$

Is this reaction possible in principle? Given the data set forth in Table 6, let us first evaluate the situation at 298°K. For the above reaction we are given ΔH^0_{298} directly, and ΔS^0_{298} we calculate as follows:

$$\Delta S^0_{298} = 46.01 - \tfrac{1}{2}(45.76) - \tfrac{3}{2}(31.21) = -23.69.$$

With the aid of equation (37) we can now calculate ΔF^0_{298}:

$$\Delta F^0_{298} = \Delta H^0_{298} - T\,\Delta S^0_{298}$$
$$= -11,040 - (298)(-23.69) = -3980 \text{ cal/mole } NH_3.$$

With the aid of equation (58) we calculate the equilibrium constant, K_{298}:

$$\log K_{298} = \frac{-\Delta F^0_{298}}{2.30\,RT} = \frac{3980}{(2.30)(1.99)(298)} = 2.92,$$

$$K_{298} = \frac{P_{NH_3}}{(P_{N_2})^{1/2}(P_{H_2})^{3/2}} = 8.3 \times 10^{+2}.$$

The equilibrium favors the production of ammonia at room temperature, but at room temperature the rate of reaction is undetectably small. What then will be the situation at higher temperatures—at 500°C, for example?

Whether we use equation (62) or equation (63) to determine the equilibrium constant at 500°C (773°K) depends on whether or not ΔH^0 remains effectively constant over the temperature range 298–773°K. Let us check this point by determining ΔH^0_{773} from the Kirchhoff relation. From the data given in Table 6 we calculate that for the reaction that forms ammonia

$$\Delta C_P = 8.52 - \tfrac{1}{2}(6.96) - \tfrac{3}{2}(6.89) = -5.29.$$

Assuming ΔC_P constant over the temperature range, we can use equation (12) to find that

$$\Delta H^0_{773} = \Delta H^0_{298} + \Delta C_P(773 - 298)$$
$$= -11,040 + (-5.29)(475) = -13,540.$$

This change in ΔH^0 is far too large to be ignored. We must then use equation (63), expressing ΔH^0, in terms of ΔC_P, as a function of temperature. But now arises this awkward question: will ΔC_P itself be constant over the range of 475°K? The answer is: almost certainly not! But is it worth while to allow for this effect in the present calculation? The ΔC_P term is, after all, only a correction term, and to make a correction in the correction may well be superfluous when the temperature range is only a few hundred degrees and when, in any case, we propose to treat as ideal gases all too real at the relatively high pressures to which we will extend our calculation. Let us reconcile ourselves to some degree of approximation in our answer; for then, taking ΔC_P as constant, we can greatly reduce the tediousness of the calculation while making no change whatever in its intrinsic nature.

Using equation (12), we express ΔH^0 as a function of temperature:

$$\Delta H^0 = \Delta H^0_{298} + \Delta C_P(T - 298).$$

Substituting this in equation (63), we find

$$d \ln K = \frac{\Delta H^0_{298} + \Delta C_P(T - 298)}{RT^2} dT$$

$$= \frac{\Delta H^0_{298} - 298\,\Delta C_P}{RT^2} dT + \frac{\Delta C_P}{RT} dT.$$

Assuming the constancy of ΔC_P, integration over the range 298 to $T°K$ involves only familiar simple integrals:

$$\int_{K_{298}}^{K_T} d \ln K = \frac{\Delta H^0_{298} - 298\,\Delta C_P}{R} \int_{298}^{T} \frac{dT}{T^2} + \frac{\Delta C_P}{R} \int_{298}^{T} \frac{dT}{T},$$

$$\ln \frac{K_T}{K_{298}} = -\frac{\Delta H^0_{298} - 298\,\Delta C_P}{R} \left(\frac{1}{T} - \frac{1}{298}\right) + \frac{\Delta C_P}{R} \ln \frac{T}{298}.$$

Shifting over to denary logarithms, and substituting numerical figures, we have

$$2.30 \log \frac{K_T}{K_{298}} = -\frac{-11{,}040 - 298(-5.29)}{1.99} \left(\frac{1}{T} - \frac{1}{298}\right)$$
$$+ \frac{-5.29}{1.99} (2.30) \log \frac{T}{298}.$$

Dividing through by 2.30, separating log terms, and cleaning up a bit, yields

$$\log K_T - \log K_{298} = \frac{11{,}040 - 1580}{(1.99)(2.30)} \left(\frac{1}{T} - \frac{1}{298}\right)$$
$$- 2.66 \log T + 2.66 \log 298.$$

Substituting the known values of $\log K_{298}$ and $\log 298$, and doing a bit more cleaning up, then yields

$$\log K_T - 2.92 = \frac{9460}{4.58} \left(\frac{1}{T} - \frac{1}{298}\right) - 2.66 \log T + (2.66)(2.47).$$

The rest is arithmetic, and the final relation is

$$\log K_T = \frac{2070}{T} - 2.66 \log T + 2.56.$$

We are now in a position to determine the equilibrium constant at 500°C, 773°K:

$$\log K_{773} = \tfrac{2070}{773} - 2.66 \log 773 + 2.56 = -2.44 = -3 + 0.56,$$
$$K_{773} = 3.6 \times 10^{-3}.$$

The value determined experimentally at 773°K is 3.8×10^{-3}. Using the approximation that ΔC_P is constant, we have extrapolated over a range of 475°K to find that the equilibrium constant is reduced by a factor of 1/250,000. Our error in determining K_{773} is only 6%—surely not a bad showing for an approximate calculation.

At 500°C the value of K looks unpropitious but, since two volumes of N_2 and H_2 combine to form one volume of NH_3, perhaps a reasonable yield of ammonia can be obtained by a synthesis at high pressure. Suppose that, working at 500°C with a stoichiometric mixture of $3H_2$ to $1N_2$, we maintain a total pressure of 100 atm. What then will be the percentage of ammonia in the equilibrium mixture? Call that percentage y—which symbol will also represent the partial pressure of NH_3, in atmospheres, in the mixture at a total pressure of 100 atm. The pressure of the H_2 and N_2 together will be $(100 - y)$ atm and, since we began with a stoichiometric mixture, the pressure of N_2 will be $\tfrac{1}{4}(100 - y)$ and the pressure of H_2 will be $\tfrac{3}{4}(100 - y)$ atm. Using the approximate value we have calculated for the equilibrium constant at 500°C, we write

$$\frac{P_{NH_3}}{(P_{N_2})^{1/2}(P_{H_2})^{3/2}} = 3.6 \times 10^{-3}.$$

Substitution then yields

$$\frac{y}{[\tfrac{1}{4}(100 - y)]^{1/2}[\tfrac{3}{4}(100 - y)]^{3/2}} = 3.6 \times 10^{-3},$$

$$\frac{y}{3\sqrt{3}\left(\dfrac{100 - y}{4}\right)^2} = 3.6 \times 10^{-3},$$

$$\frac{y}{(100 - y)^2} = \frac{5.2}{16} \times 3.6 \times 10^{-3} = 1.17 \times 10^{-3}.$$

This reduces to the following quadratic equation:

$$y^2 - 1.05 \times 10^3 y + 10^4 = 0.$$

Solving, we find the equilibrium partial pressure to be ~ 9.6 atm, compared with the experimental value of 10.4 atm (or 10.4%). Our doubly approximate method (taking ΔC_P as constant and treating real gases as ideal) thus yields a result amply good enough to support appraisal of the technologic feasibility of this NH_3 synthesis.

Epilogue: Remarks on Science and the Social Order

Haber began his studies of the synthesis of ammonia in 1904. On the basis of calculations like that given above, confirmed by a great many experiments, he came to conceive the process for which he took the key patent in 1908. This patent describes a continuous recirculation of the process gas—using heat exchangers but maintaining throughout the same high pressure—in such fashion that even a low equilibrium concentration of ammonia is removed continuously, by condensation, while the remaining process gas is reheated and passed again over the catalyst. By 1909 Haber was able to demonstrate, to a representative of the Badische Anilin und Sodafabrik, a tiny pilot system producing about 80 grams of liquid ammonia per hour. The many remaining problems of the synthesis were solved in the laboratories of this concern which—five years later, in 1914—had managed to bring the Haber process into quantity production.

That date is significant. All the high explosives used in the World War of 1914–18—*nitro*glycerine (for dynamite, etc.), *nitro*cellulose ("guncotton"), tri*nitro*toluene (TNT), tri*nitro*phenol (picric acid), etc.—absolutely require for their manufacture the use of nitric acid which, at the outbreak of the World War I, was derived almost exclusively from Chile saltpeter, $NaNO_3$. A country cut off from its supply of this mineral, as Germany was by the British blockade, could, however, still obtain nitric acid if only it could fix atmospheric nitrogen as ammonia, since ammonia can be converted to nitric acid by a series of steps summarized in the equation

$$NH_3 + 2O_2 = HNO_3 + H_2O.$$

The Haber process was brought into production not a minute too early for Germany. Coates writes:

> The sole source of nitric acid in Germany at that time was imported Chile saltpeter, and the stock of this material was so low that the war might have ended in a few months but for the discovery of some 50,000 tons of nitrate at the Antwerp docks. Even this could give but a short respite . . . Beginning in 1913 with an output of about 6500 metric tons (of fixed nitrogen), the production of synthetic ammonia was roughly doubled in each successive year until at the end of the war it reached the huge figure of some 200,000 tons per annum. Without synthetic ammonia it is very improbable that Germany could have carried on the war as long as she did, and in this sense it may be said that Haber saved his country from premature defeat.

Is it a blessing so to be saved? Prolongation of the war so depleted

Germany, and so embittered her foes, that the postwar situation may be thought to have made inevitable the rise of a Hitler. If this be so, the Haber process was no blessing for Germany, and certainly no blessing for Haber, who, with the rise of Hitler, became "the Jew Haber" driven to his death in exile.

In the late 19th century there were prophets of disaster who foretold the early doom of urban civilization, an early resurgence of chronic famine, consequent to the ultimately inevitable exhaustion of the supply of Chile saltpeter, the major source of fixed nitrogen for agricultural fertilizer. The Haber process frees us once and for all from this threat—and it does so in no uncertain terms. Current U.S. production of Haber-process ammonia approximates 5,000,000 tons per annum, and the vast bulk of this goes into use as fertilizer. All over the world this kind of technological exploitation of science makes possible a life of greater abundance for a greater number of people than ever before. But always such exploitations give rise also to less attractive possibilities. In this country the accumulation of crop surpluses draws Sir Bagby's comment: "It's not the wheat that gets you; it's the stupidity." And in the world at large the population explosion seems today to open the possibility of an ultimate disaster in some sense converse of that foretold at the end of the 19th century.

Science a curse, its exploitation bringing death and disaster? It may be so. But life is commonly esteemed the supreme blessing, and *most of us* would not now be alive save for the exploitations of science in industry, agriculture, and medicine. What would you? Ambivalence attaches to the works of science simply because their technologic exploitations rest in the hands of men. Says Nagel:

> . . . an opportunity does not determine the use that men make of it; and except on the assumption that the quality of human life is enhanced when alternatives to traditional forms of conduct are kept at a minimum, it is childish to bewail the expansion of science as the chief source of our current evils.

The *scientist* makes an ethical judgment, and assumes a moral responsibility, when he elects to participate in the technologic exploitation of science for destructive purposes. "Social demand" may applaud, but cannot justify, such a decision—any more than it can the decision of the smith who turns iron into swords rather than ploughshares. But *science*, scientific knowledge, is ethically as neutral as iron: "evil" only when men forge it as a sword; "good" when beaten into a ploughshare. Conceivably there is some knowledge that can lead only to "evil"; certainly there is none that can lead only to "good." The discovery of some marvelous vaccine against a previously lethal plague would seem wholly "good," but it opens up brand new possibilities for "evil": an aggressor will wage germ warfare only if he possesses means to protect his own population. One can never deny the possibility of what Sophocles thought a certainty: "No great thing ever enters human life without a curse." Unlike the Greeks, however, we have an abiding faith in the possibility of ameliorating the human condition which emboldens us to push on in science, and elsewhere, with Whitehead's conviction that: "Panic of error is the death of progress."

Supplementary Readings

Historical

CARNOT, SADI, *Reflections on the Motive Power of Fire;* ed. E. Mendoza, with other papers by E. Clapeyron and R. Clausius. New York: Dover, 1960.

CHALMERS, T. W., *Historic Researches.* London: Morgan Bros., 1949. Chapter 2: "The Mechanical Equivalent of Heat."

Technological

SANDFORT, J. F., "Heat Pumps," *Scientific American* **184,** 54 (May 1951).

AUSTIN, L. G., "Fuel Cells," *ibid.* **201,** 72 (October 1959).

Experimental

STURTEVANT, J. M., "Calorimetry" in *Physical Methods of Organic Chemistry,* ed. A. Weissberger, vol. 1, part 1, pp. 523–654. New York: Interscience, 1959.

Conceptual

DARROW, K. K., "The Concept of Entropy," *American Journal of Physics* **12,** 183 (1944).

DYSON, F. J., "What is Heat?" *Scientific American* **191,** 58 (September 1954).

BLATT, J. M., "Time Reversal," *ibid.* **195,** 107 (August 1956).

BLUM, H. F., *Time's Arrow and Evolution.* Princeton: University Press, 1951.

FERMI, E., *Thermodynamics.* New York: Dover, 1956.

CALDIN, E. F., *Introduction to Chemical Thermodynamics.* Oxford: University Press, 1958.

WALL, F. T., *Chemical Thermodynamics.* San Francisco: Freeman, 1958.

Appendix I*
Some Operations of the Calculus

To follow completely all the derivations in this book, you need grasp only a very few of the most elementary concepts and relations of the calculus. All these mathematical tools are developed in the present appendix, in which we represent a general "function" as $y = f(x)$, read: "y equals f of x." This does not signify that y is f times x, but simply that y is so expressed in terms of x that, when x is given, the value of y is also determined. Some simple functions are $y = 2x$, $y = 1/x$, $y = \sin x$.

Differentiation. Consider the changing velocity of an automobile accelerating, from a standing start, along a straight road. Figure A–1 shows the velocity plotted as a function of time.

Suppose we wish to know the acceleration—that is, the rate at which the velocity is changing—at time t_0. Experimentally we might read the velocity once at time t_0 and again at some later time t_3. Then

$$\frac{v_3 - v_0}{t_3 - t_0} = \frac{\Delta_3 v}{\Delta_3 t} = \alpha_3$$

and we may say that this quotient represents the rate of change of the velocity at time t_0. But clearly this is *not the instantaneous* acceleration at time t_0—represented by the slope (i.e., the vertical "rise" over the horizontal "run") of the tangent to the curve at point (t_0, v_0)—but rather

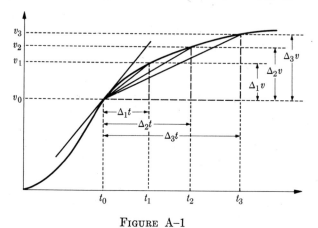

FIGURE A–1

---

* For a full, and impeccable, account of the arguments sketched in this Appendix see G. B. Thomas, *Calculus and Analytic Geometry*, 3rd ed., pp. 17–19, 50–63, 82–87, 155–162, 181–199. Reading, Mass.: Addison-Wesley, 1960.

the *average* acceleration over the period t_0 to t_3 represented by the slope of the secant line from (t_0, v_0) to (t_3, v_3). We come closer to the instantaneous acceleration represented by the tangent line if we make our terminal velocity measurement at time t_2, and still closer if we can make the measurement at time t_1, but clearly we will get an accurate value only when the time interval becomes infinitesimal, in which case the second velocity will differ infinitesimally (and wholly undetectably) from the first. How then are we to proceed?

We want the value of $\Delta v/\Delta t$ as $\Delta t \to 0$ (read "delta t approaches zero"). This value of the instantaneous acceleration we cannot get directly from readings of stopwatch and speedometer. However, given such readings, we can prepare a graph like that of Fig. A–1. By actually constructing the tangent line, we can determine its slope and take this as the instantaneous acceleration. There is nothing wrong in principle with this somewhat clumsy procedure, and on some occasions it may be the only option open to us. But when v can be expressed as an analytical function of t, the differential calculus offers a much more elegant approach to the problem.

Suppose that $v = mt - nt^2$, where m and n are constants. At the instant t_0, the velocity $v_0 = mt_0 - nt_0^2$. After the lapse of the further time interval Δt the velocity at time $t_0 + \Delta t$ will be given by the equation

$$v_0 + \Delta v = m(t_0 + \Delta t) - n(t_0 + \Delta t)^2$$
$$= m(t_0 + \Delta t) - n(t_0^2 + 2t_0 \Delta t + \overline{\Delta t^2}).$$

To find the actual change of velocity, Δv, in the time interval Δt, we subtract from the last equation the expression for the initial condition:

$$v_0 = mt_0 - nt_0^2.$$

We have then

$$\Delta v = m \Delta t - n(2t_0 \Delta t + \overline{\Delta t^2}).$$

Now we are interested in the limiting value of the ratio $\Delta v/\Delta t$, and to form the ratio we divide through the last equation by Δt, to get

$$\frac{\Delta v}{\Delta t} = m - n(2t_0 + \Delta t).$$

As such, the ratio $\Delta v/\Delta t$ gives us the slope not of the tangent line but of a secant; but as $\Delta t \to 0$ the value of this ratio approaches as a limit the slope of the tangent line. What is that slope? Looking at the last equation, we see that any term containing Δt in the numerator will go to zero as $\Delta t \to 0$. Hence

$$\lim_{\Delta t \to 0} \left[\frac{\Delta v}{\Delta t} \right] = \lim_{\Delta t \to 0} [m - n(2t_0 + \Delta t)] = m - 2nt_0.$$

This is the expression for the slope of the tangent line at t_0. Since t_0 can be *any* point on the curve, we have only to insert any particular value of t_0 to read off from the last formula the instantaneous acceleration at that time. And to the term

$$\lim_{\Delta t \to 0} \left[\frac{\Delta v}{\Delta t} \right]$$

we assign the special symbol dv/dt (read, "the derivative of v with respect to t"):

$$\frac{dv}{dt} = m - 2nt.$$

This somewhat tedious procedure for determining the slope can be generalized, so that one need not go through the entire procedure in other similar cases. Consider what we have done:

1. We wrote down the function $v = f(t)$.
2. We formulated the expression $v + \Delta v = f(t + \Delta t)$.
3. We subtracted the first expression from the second to get $\Delta v = f(t + \Delta t) - f(t)$.
4. We divided through by Δt to get

$$\frac{\Delta v}{\Delta t} = \frac{f(t + \Delta t) - f(t)}{\Delta t}.$$

The division by Δt can only be indicated when we speak of the general function, $f(t)$, but would actually be carried through, as in the example, when dealing with any specific function.

5. We took the limit as $\Delta t \to 0$, and so arrived at the derivative:

$$\frac{dv}{dt} = \lim_{\Delta t \to 0} \left[\frac{f(t + \Delta t) - f(t)}{\Delta t} \right].$$

This is the *general* procedure for determining an instantaneous rate of change. [*Note:* For Newton, what we call the calculus was the method of fluxions, from L. *fluxio(-onis)*, a flowing.] There is, of course, no reason to restrict the variables to v and t, and for the general function $y = f(x)$ we write a similar expression for the instantaneous rate of change of y with x:

$$\frac{dy}{dx} = \lim_{\Delta x \to 0} \left[\frac{f(x + \Delta x) - f(x)}{\Delta x} \right]. \qquad \textit{Definition}$$

For the bracketed expression we will in the future use the more compact expression $f'(x)$ (read "f prime of x"), so that when $y = f(x)$ then $dy/dx = f'(x)$.

Given the above definition, we can at once write down the derivatives of a great many simple functions.

If $y = x^3$; then $\dfrac{dy}{dx} = \lim\limits_{\Delta x \to 0} \left[\dfrac{(x^3 + 3x^2 \,\Delta x + 3x \,\overline{\Delta x}^2 + \overline{\Delta x}^3) - x^3}{\Delta x} \right]$

$\qquad = \lim\limits_{\Delta x \to 0} [3x^2 + 3x \,\Delta x + \overline{\Delta x}^2] = 3x^2.$

If $y = x^4$; then $\dfrac{dy}{dx} = \lim\limits_{\Delta x \to 0} \left[\dfrac{(x^4 + 4x^3 \,\Delta x + 6x^2 \,\overline{\Delta x}^2 + 4x \,\overline{\Delta x}^3 + \overline{\Delta x}^4) - x^4}{\Delta x} \right]$

$\qquad = \lim\limits_{\Delta x \to 0} [4x^3 + 6x^2 \,\Delta x + 4x \,\overline{\Delta x}^2 + \overline{\Delta x}^3] = 4x^3.$

These results, together with that earlier obtained in the illustrative example, suffice to suggest what can indeed be shown to be a general formula. For all integral values of n, positive or negative:

$$\text{If } y = x^n, \qquad \text{then } \frac{dy}{dx} = nx^{n-1}.$$

The illustrative example suggests also two further conclusions the (easy) proofs of which are omitted. First,

$$\text{If } y = x^m + x^n, \qquad \text{then } \frac{dy}{dx} = mx^{m-1} + nx^{n-1}.$$

And, more generally still,

$$\text{If } y = f(x) + g(x), \qquad \text{then } \frac{dy}{dx} = f'(x) + g'(x).$$

Second, if we take C to be any constant term, then

$$\text{If } y = Cx^n, \qquad \text{then } \frac{dy}{dx} = (C)(n)x^{n-1}.$$

And, much more generally still,

$$\text{If } y = Cf(x), \qquad \text{then } \frac{dy}{dx} = Cf'(x).$$

These formulas give us an easy means of finding the slopes of curves—and, much more generally, the rate of change of one variable with another in a great many cases of practical interest. For our work in thermodynamics we need only three more formulas. The first is almost trivial. Suppose that $y = C$. This is the equation of a straight line parallel to the x-axis, and so with slope zero at all points. The use of the basic definition further confirms the conclusion that

$$\text{If } y = C, \qquad \text{then } \frac{dy}{dx} = 0.$$

The next relation is simply announced, not derived. We are most used to denary logarithms that satisfy the definition $x = 10^{\log x}$. Another set of logarithms is founded on the base $e = 2.718\ldots$, and satisfies the definition $x = e^{\ln x}$. The two sets of logarithms are related by the equation $2.303 \log x = \ln x$. Logarithms to the base e are far less convenient for, say, ordinary trigonometric calculations, but they have important mathematical properties, one of which is

$$\text{If } y = \ln x, \quad \text{then } \frac{dy}{dx} = \frac{1}{x}.$$

One last relation:

$$\text{If } y = f(x) \cdot g(x), \quad \text{then } \frac{dy}{dx} = f(x) \cdot g'(x) + g(x) \cdot f'(x).$$

This we can prove with the aid of the basic definition. Letting $f(x) = u$ and $g(x) = v$, we rewrite the function in the form $y = uv$. Now, by definition,

$$\frac{dy}{dx} = \lim_{\Delta x \to 0} \left[\frac{(u + \Delta u)(v + \Delta v) - uv}{\Delta x} \right]$$

$$= \lim_{\Delta x \to 0} \left[\frac{uv + u\,\Delta v + v\,\Delta u + \Delta u\,\Delta v - uv}{\Delta x} \right]$$

$$= \lim_{\Delta x \to 0} \left[u\,\frac{\Delta v}{\Delta x} + v\,\frac{\Delta u}{\Delta x} + \Delta u\,\frac{\Delta v}{\Delta x} \right].$$

But when Δx approaches zero so will Δu and Δv. For consider that

$$\lim (\Delta u) = \lim \left(\frac{\Delta u}{\Delta x}\,\Delta x \right) = \lim \left(\frac{\Delta u}{\Delta x} \right) \lim (\Delta x) = \left(\frac{du}{dx} \right)(0) = 0.$$

Consequently it follows that

$$\frac{dy}{dx} = u\,\frac{dv}{dx} + v\,\frac{du}{dx} + 0\,\frac{dv}{dx}$$

$$= u\,\frac{dv}{dx} + v\,\frac{du}{dx}.$$

But by definition

$$u = f(x) \quad \text{and} \quad \frac{du}{dx} = f'(x),$$

and also

$$v = g(x) \quad \text{and} \quad \frac{dv}{dx} = g'(x).$$

Substituting in the previous equation we have then what we set out to prove:

$$\frac{dy}{dx} = f(x) \cdot g'(x) + g(x) \cdot f'(x).$$

The derivative dy/dx, as so far considered, is a single symbol and not a fraction. But when x is an independent variable and y is a function of x, we can attach meaning to dy and dx separately. For the function $y = f(x)$ we have

$$\frac{dy}{dx} = f'(x).$$

Then dx ("the differential of x") is to be regarded as an infinitesimal increment in x, and dy ("the differential of y") is a function of x and dx given by

$$dy = f'(x)\, dx.$$

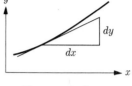

FIGURE A-2

That is, dy/dx is the *rate* at which y changes per unit change in x, and then dy is the *amount* by which y changes (measured along the tangent to the curve) per unit change in x. If dx is held to infinitesimal values, the tangent line diverges only infinitesimally from the curve, and dy becomes simply the infinitesimal increment in y corresponding to the infinitesimal increment dx.

Function	Derivative	Differential	Example
$y = C$	$\dfrac{dy}{dx} = \dfrac{d(C)}{dx} = 0$	$dy = d(C) = 0$	$d(C) = 0$
$y = x^n$	$\dfrac{dy}{dx} = \dfrac{d(x^n)}{dx} = nx^{n-1}$	$dy = d(x^n) = nx^{n-1}\, dx$	$d(x^{-1}) = -\dfrac{dx}{x^2}$
$y = \ln x$	$\dfrac{dy}{dx} = \dfrac{d(\ln x)}{dx} = \dfrac{1}{x}$	$dy = d(\ln x) = \dfrac{dx}{x}$	$d(\ln x) = \dfrac{dx}{x}$
$y = Cu$	$\dfrac{dy}{dx} = \dfrac{d(Cu)}{dx} = C\dfrac{du}{dx}$	$dy = d(Cu) = C\, du$	$d(12x^2) = 24x\, dx$
$y = u + v$	$\dfrac{dy}{dx} = \dfrac{d(u + v)}{dx} = \dfrac{du}{dx} + \dfrac{dv}{dx}$	$dy = d(u + v) = du + dv$	$d(x^2 + x^3) = 2x\, dx + 3x^2\, dx$
$y = uv$	$\dfrac{dy}{dx} = \dfrac{d(uv)}{dx} = u\dfrac{dv}{dx} + v\dfrac{du}{dx}$	$dy = d(uv) = v\, du + u\, dv$	$d(x \ln x) = \ln x\, dx + dx$

Integration. The plot of velocity, as a function of time, for a car accelerating from rest is again depicted in Fig. A–3(a). We now raise this question: what is the total *distance* covered by the car in any period of

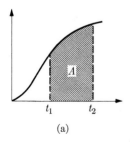

(a)

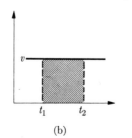

(b)

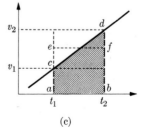

(c)

FIGURE A-3

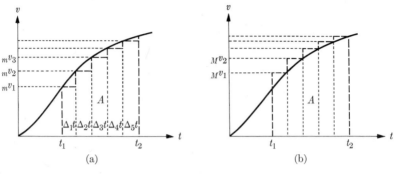

FIGURE A-4

time, say in the interval t_1 to t_2? Now there are two cases in which this question poses no difficulty. If in the interval t_1 to t_2 the car proceeds at constant velocity, as shown in Fig. A–3(b), then the distance traversed is simply the product of the velocity and the elapsed time, or $v(t_2 - t_1)$. Note that this product is just the shaded area in Fig. A–3(b). An only slightly less simple case is that in which velocity changes uniformly with time, so that the plot of v against t is a line of constant slope, as shown in Fig. A–3(c). Here we easily find the distance traversed by forming the product of the *average* velocity and the time interval, or

$$\frac{v_1 + v_2}{2} (t_2 - t_1).$$

By so doing, we determine the area $\overline{aefb}$ which is equal to the shaded area $\overline{acdb}$ enclosed between the velocity plot, the x-axis, and the verticals corresponding to the limits t_1 and t_2.

Returning now to the original problem sketched in Fig. A–3(a), we see that here too the shaded area will correspond to the distance sought. Consider that we divide the period t_1 to t_2 into a number of equal short increments of time, Δt. Although the car's velocity changes continuously as a function of time, for the short interval $\Delta_i t$ we may think to approximate the velocity, as shown in Fig. A–4(a), as the initial (minimum) velocity $_mv_i$ for that interval. The distance covered in the time interval is then $_mv_i (\Delta_i t)$, which is simply the area of one rectangular block. For the total distance covered we will, according to this mode of reckoning, add the areas of all the rectangular blocks falling between t_1 and t_2. A compact symbolization of this operation is $\sum_{i=1}^{5} {}_mv_i (\Delta_i t)$, where the Greek sigma instructs us to make the indicated summation of all the individual terms having the indicated form. And it seems intuitively evident that as the standard interval $\Delta t \to 0$ and as the number n of ever-narrower blocks is increased without limit, this sum will approach as a limit the area enclosed under the curve between the verticals at t_1 and t_2. That is,

$$A = \lim_{\Delta t \to 0} \sum_{i=1}^{n} {}_{m}v_i \, (\Delta_i t).$$

One may perhaps have an uneasy feeling that this mode of approach yields only an *approximation*, a minimum value for the area under the curve. But consider that we may also set out, as shown in Fig. A–4(b), from the final (maximum) velocity, ${}_{M}v_i$, attained in each time interval. For the total distance traveled we have then the approximation

$$\sum_{i=1}^{5} {}_{M}v_i \, (\Delta_i t).$$

And if now again we shorten the time interval, and so increase without limit the number of blocks, n, it seems clear that in this case too we can write

$$A = \lim_{\Delta t \to 0} \sum_{i=1}^{n} {}_{M}v_i \, (\Delta_i t).$$

That is, whether we approach from the direction of an *over*estimate or from the direction of an *under*estimate, in the limit we approach the same area. Given a plot of velocity as a function of time we can then determine, right on the graph, the distance traversed in the period t_1 to t_2 simply by counting up squares in the enclosed region. This geometric approach—perfectly effective, and often unavoidable—falls in the same category of (crude) operations as the determination of a slope by actual construction of a tangent line. In the latter case we found a more elegant alternative, the analytical operation of differentiation, available whenever the plotted curve can be expressed as a function $y = f(x)$. In exactly the same way, *integration* furnishes us with an analytical method for the determination of areas enclosed under curves that can be expressed in the functional form $y = f(x)$.

Let us consider the general case of a changing velocity expressible as $v = f(t)$, making no assumption of a constantly increasing velocity. Taking some standard short time interval Δt, we ask what will be the distance ΔA covered in the period between some particular time t and the time $t + \Delta t$. We take as the velocity *throughout* this time interval the value $v = f(t)$, and it makes no difference whether this is a maximum, a minimum, or an intermediate value for the velocity in the indicated period. For, as we have just seen, as $\Delta t \to 0$ the maximum and minimum values of v in the ever-decreasing time interval are simply "squeezed" towards each other and towards the value $v = f(t)$. As an approximation for the distance covered we have then the thin rectangular slice cut out by the vertical boundaries at t and $t + \Delta t$, with area $\Delta A = v \, \Delta t = f(t) \cdot \Delta t$.

And as a rigorous result we have, in the limit as $\Delta t \to 0$, that

$$\lim_{\Delta t \to 0} \left[\frac{\Delta A}{\Delta t} \right] = \frac{dA}{dt} = f(t).$$

Now we are seeking the *entire* distance covered in the period t_1 to t_2— the entire area enclosed under the plot between the vertical boundaries at t_1 and t_2. We seek then some relation of the form $A = F(t)$ from which we can evaluate, as a function of time, the total distance concerned. Given a relation we write in differential form as $dA = f(t)\,dt$, we seek the desired relation. Clearly, we must somehow "dis-differentiate" or "un-differentiate." This operation we call integration and symbolize $\int$. We write then

$$\int dA = \int f(t)\,dt.$$

Bidden by the integral sign, we ask ourselves what function of A will, when differentiated, yield the term dA. The answer is surely obvious, and we then write

$$A = \int f(t)\,dt.$$

What about the right side of the equation? We see that the $F(t)$ we seek must be that function of t which on differentiation yields the term $f(t)\,dt$. That is,

$$f(t) = F'(t).$$

That integration is just the inverse of differentiation we can then symbolize as follows:

$$\int f(t)\,dt = \int F'(t)\,dt = \int dF(t) = F(t).$$

Given $f(t)$, we hope to establish $F(t)$. Take the particular case with which we began—that of an accelerating car for which $v = mt - nt^2$. We then write

$$A = \int f(t)\,dt = \int (mt - nt^2)\,dt.$$

What function of t will, when differentiated, yield $(mt - nt^2)\,dt$? Try the first term first:

Differentiation of t^2 yields $2t\,dt$.
Differentiation of $\frac{1}{2}t^2$ yields $t\,dt$.
Differentiation of $(m)(\frac{1}{2})t^2$ yields $mt\,dt$.

A similar development yields the further conclusion that

Differentiation of $(n)(\frac{1}{3})t^3$ yields $nt^2\,dt$.

Hence we can at last write

$$A = \frac{mt^2}{2} - \frac{nt^3}{3}, \tag{a}$$

and our problem is at last solved. Or is it?

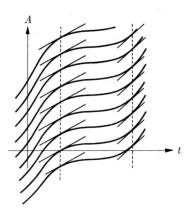

FIGURE A-5

Consider again the differential equation $dA/dt = f(t)$. Observe that it can correspond to any of the whole family of curves sketched in Fig. A-5. All the equation tells us is that the *slope* of a plot of A against t is a particular function of t, and any of an infinite number of curves will meet this requirement. By re-examining the last derivation, we see that in fact we have oversimplified: we do *not* have a unique solution for A. The equation

$$dA = (mt - nt^2)\, dt$$

can be obtained not only from equation (a) but also from all equations of the form

$$A = \frac{mt^2}{2} - \frac{nt^3}{3} + C,$$

where C can be *any constant* since, as earlier noted, $d(C) = 0$. For different values of C the last equation produces the set of parallel curves shown in Fig. A-5. For any given value of t, A may then assume any one of the infinite possibilities corresponding to any one of the infinite values that C may take. Our problem is then *not* fully solved; we must somehow establish along which one of the curves $A = F(t) + C$ we are to read.

We easily meet this apparently difficult problem by a specification of "limits"—corresponding to the vertical lines bounding the interval in question. Suppose, for example, we wish to determine the distance traveled by the car in the period beginning at time 0, when it starts from rest, and ending at some later time t. At the "lower" (beginning) limit, when $t = 0$, the distance traversed will be $A = 0$, and we seek the value of A at time t. We display the limits in the form

$$\int_0^A dA = \int_0^t (mt - nt^2)\, dt. \qquad \text{(b)}$$

This specification of limits at once establishes a choice of one of the curves $A = F(t) + C$: we must select the curve running through the origin ($A = 0$ when $t = 0$), and along this curve we can then read off the value of A corresponding to any specified time t.

The geometric operation here described in words is easily reduced to a rigorously specifiable analytical operation. Treating the general case, suppose we wish to know the distance traveled by the car in the time between t_1 and t_2. Let A_1 represent the distance (relative to some arbitrary standard) at time t_1; let A_2 represent the distance at time t_2. What we then want to find is $A_2 - A_1$. We begin by substituting the lower set of limits to establish the value of the constant C:

$$A_1 = \frac{mt_1^2}{2} - \frac{nt_1^3}{3} + C,$$

whence

$$C = A_1 - \left(\frac{mt_1^2}{2} - \frac{nt_1^3}{3}\right).$$

Having obtained this value of C, we can now demand that at the "upper" limit

$$A_2 = \frac{mt_2^2}{2} - \frac{nt_2^3}{3} + \left\{A_1 - \left(\frac{mt_1^2}{2} - \frac{nt_1^3}{3}\right)\right\}.$$

This, on rearrangement, yields

$$A_2 - A_1 = \left(\frac{mt_2^2}{2} - \frac{nt_2^3}{3}\right) - \left(\frac{mt_1^2}{2} - \frac{nt_1^3}{3}\right).$$

Here is an expression for the distance traveled in the period t_1 to t_2. At last we have solved our problem.

The somewhat clumsy procedure in which we solve, and substitute, for C is easily avoided. Returning to equation (b), we integrate and indicate the limits thus:

$$A\Big]_{A_1}^{A_2} = \frac{mt^2}{2} - \frac{nt^3}{3}\Big]_{t_1}^{t_2}.$$

On each side of the equation we simply subtract from the value of the function at the upper limit, the value of the function at the lower limit, and so at once obtain the relation previously secured more laboriously:

$$A_2 - A_1 = \left(\frac{mt_2^2}{2} - \frac{nt_2^3}{3}\right) - \left(\frac{mt_1^2}{2} - \frac{nt_1^3}{3}\right).$$

And now we may see our way to a general formulation of the operation of integration. Any time we can relate the change of one variable to that of another through an equation of the type $dA = f(x)\,dx$, then we can always conclude that, for the limits (x_1, A_1) and (x_2, A_2), it is the case that

$$A_2 - A_1 = F(x_2) - F(x_1),$$

where $F(x)$ is the function that, on differentiation, yields the function $f(x)\,dx$.

We close with a few specific formulas for the determination of $F(x)$ from $f(x)$. We have already encountered examples of the general relation

$$\int_{x_1}^{x_2} x^m\,dx = \frac{x^{m+1}}{m+1}\bigg]_{x_1}^{x_2}$$

and also of

$$\int_{x_1}^{x_2} [f(x)\,dx + g(x)\,dx] = F(x) + G(x)\bigg]_{x_1}^{x_2}.$$

Two more formulas follow, just as these first two do, directly from the tabulation on page 97. The first is

$$\int_{x_1}^{x_2} \frac{dx}{x} = \ln x\bigg]_{x_1}^{x_2} = \ln x_2 - \ln x_1 = \ln \frac{x_2}{x_1}.$$

The second, often a very helpful relation, indicates that integrals can always be simplified by moving constants, but *only* constants, across the integral sign:

$$\int_{x_1}^{x_2} Cf(x)\,dx = C\int_{x_1}^{x_2} f(x)\,dx = CF(x)\bigg]_{x_1}^{x_2} = C[F(x_2) - F(x_1)].$$

One last relation is of a different sort, though scarcely less obvious than the foregoing. What happens when we "invert limits"? We then have

$$\int_{x_1}^{x_2} f(x)\,dx = F(x_2) - F(x_1), \qquad \int_{x_2}^{x_1} f(x)\,dx = F(x_1) - F(x_2),$$

whence it follows that

$$\int_{x_1}^{x_2} f(x)\,dx = -\int_{x_2}^{x_1} f(x)\,dx.$$

Appendix II
Problems

Avogadro's number, $N = 6.02 \times 10^{23}$

The Faraday, $\mathcal{F} = 9.65 \times 10^4$ coul/equiv

Acceleration due to gravity, $g = 980.7$ cm/sec^2

1 atm $= 760$ mm Hg $= 1.033$ kgm/cm^2

$0°C = 273.15°K$

1 calorie $= 4.18$ joules	$R = 1.99$ cal/mole·°K
$\quad\quad\quad = 4.18$ watt-sec	$\quad = 8.31$ joules/mole·°K
$\quad\quad\quad = 4.18 \times 10^7$ ergs	$\quad = 0.0821$ liter-atm/mole·°K
$\quad\quad\quad = 0.0413$ liter-atm	

1. Between room temperature and its melting point at 327°C, lead has a specific heat of $\sim$0.033 cal/gm·°C.

(a) A bullet at an initial temperature of 20°C is stopped by impact with an unyielding target. Assuming no loss of heat from the bullet to the target, how fast must the bullet be traveling if it is just brought to its melting point by the impact?

(b) Assume that a slow-burning propellant charge maintains a substantially constant pressure in the gun barrel during the period in which the bullet is expelled. Suppose that a 10-gm slug is expelled from a barrel whose volume is 100 cm^3, with the velocity calculated in (a). What is the propulsive pressure in the gun barrel?

2. (a) During expansion against a constant external pressure of 1 atm, a gas absorbs 50 cal while its volume increases from 1 to 10 liters. What is the net change in its internal energy consequent to this expansion?

(b) A powerful steel spring weighing 55.8 gm is squeezed 2 cm shorter by a force averaging 100 kgf ($=9800$ newtons). Given that $\sim$21 kcal are liberated by the solution of 1 gm-atom of iron in dilute hydrochloric acid, what would have to be the percentage accuracy of calorimetric measurements designed to detect the increase in the internal energy of the spring as a difference in the heats of solution of the stressed spring and an otherwise identical unstressed spring?

3. (a) On the occasion of his honeymoon excursion to Switzerland, J. P. Joule is said to have rejoiced in the discovery that the water at the base of a waterfall is perceptibly warmer than at its top. Assuming that he carried a thermometer sensitive enough to show a temperature difference of 0.1°C, what was the minimum height of the waterfall he visited?

(b) A corpulent man, with mass 100 kgm, seeks to compensate for putting several lumps of sugar in his breakfast coffee by climbing the almost vertical rocks alongside the waterfall of part (a). His (typical animal) metabolism permits the conversion into work of approximately $\frac{1}{4}$ the heat of cumbustion of his food. Given that the heat of combustion of cane sugar is 1350 cal/gm, how many grams of sugar suffice to furnish the energy for his climb?

4. At 25°C and constant pressure, 326.7 kcal are released in the combustion of one mole of ethanol according to the equation

$$C_2H_5OH \text{ (l)} + 3O_2 \text{ (g)} = 2CO_2 \text{ (g)} + 3H_2O \text{ (l)}.$$

(a) For the reaction, as written, what is the value of ΔH? of ΔE?

(b) At 25°C, 10.5 kcal are required to vaporize a mole of water. If in the above reaction the water had been obtained not as liquid but as gas, what then would have been the value of ΔH? of ΔE?

(c) At 25°C and constant pressure ΔH_f for H_2O (l) is -68.3 kcal/mole, and ΔH_f for CO_2 (g) is -94.1 kcal/mole. Calculate ΔH_f for C_2H_5OH (l) under these conditions.

(d) For C_2H_5OH (g) the value of ΔH_f is -56.2 kcal at 25°C and constant pressure. For the vaporization of 1 mole of ethanol under these conditions, what is the value of ΔH? of ΔE?

5. (a) Exactly 0.005 gm-atom ($\sim$0.3 gm) of metallic zinc is dissolved in dilute aqueous hydrochloric acid in an ice calorimeter. At 0°C the specific volume of H_2O (l) is 1.001 cm^3/gm, the specific volume of H_2O (s) is 1.091 cm^3/gm, and the heat of fusion of ice is 80 cal/gm. The heat released as the zinc dissolves melts enough ice to produce a volume contraction of 0.169 cm^3 in the ice-and-water mixture surrounding the reaction vessel. Per gm-atom of zinc dissolved, calculate ΔH for the reaction

$$Zn \text{ (s)} + 2H^+ \text{ (aq)} = Zn^{++} \text{ (aq)} + H_2 \text{ (g)}.$$

(b) A similar determination is conducted with 0.005 mole of ZnO, added to the same volume of aqueous HCl of the same dilution, and we thus find $\Delta H = -15.3$ kcal for the reaction $ZnO \text{ (s)} + 2H^+ \text{ (aq)} = Zn^{++} \text{ (aq)} + H_2O \text{ (l)}$. Given that for H_2O (l) $\Delta H_f = -68.3$ kcal/mole at 0°C, calculate the heat of formation of ZnO—that is, ΔH for the reaction $Zn \text{ (s)} + \frac{1}{2}O_2 \text{ (g)} = ZnO \text{ (s)}$.

(c) The calculation in part (b) involves a major implicit assumption—well justified in the present case by good agreement of the calculated value with that measured directly. What is that assumption?

6. At 100°C the heat of vaporization of water is 9.7 kcal/mole, and the heat capacities of liquid and vapor are respectively $\sim$18 and 8 cal/mole·°C.

(a) Use Kirchhoff's equation to estimate the heat of vaporization of water at 25°C.

(b) Although the result obtained in (a) is in fair agreement with the correct value ($\sim$10.5 kcal), this use of Kirchhoff's equation is fundamentally invalid. Why?

7. (a) A stoichiometric mixture of gaseous hydrogen with air (taken as 80% N_2 and 20% O_2) is fed through the nozzle of a torch. Assume an initial temperature of 298°K and a pressure constant throughout at 1 atm; assume further that there is no loss of heat from the flame to the surroundings. For H_2O (g) take C_P as 9 cal/mole·°C, for N_2 (g) take C_P as 7 cal/mole·°C, and for the over-all reaction take

$$H_2 \text{ (g)} + \tfrac{1}{2}O_2 \text{ (g)} = H_2O \text{ (g)}, \qquad \Delta H = -58 \text{ kcal}.$$

Noting that both H_2O (g) and N_2 (g) are present after the combustion, calculate the peak temperature achievable.

(b) To fuse a patch over a rent in the high melting envelope of my space ship I use a torch that sprays the metal with a stream of atomic hydrogen, produced by passing H_2 (g) through an electric field. The reaction produced as the atomic hydrogen hits the metal is

$$2H \text{ (g)} = H_2 \text{ (g)}, \quad \Delta H = -104 \text{ kcal.}$$

Assuming constant (low) pressure, 100% efficiency in the generation of H (g), and no heat loss to the surroundings, and taking as C_P for H_2 (g) a value of 7 cal/mole·°C, calculate the maximum temperature rise I can produce with my torch.

(c) The actually attainable peak temperature is far less than that calculated in (b). To what limitation(s) *in principle* would you attribute the discrepancy of calculated and attained temperatures?

8. A stoichiometric mixture of methane, CH_4, and air is exploded in a sealed bomb. Assuming no heat loss to the walls of the bomb, and taking air as 20% O_2 and 80% N_2, the initial temperature as 25°C and the initial pressure as 1 atm, take as the values of C_V for N_2 (g) 5 cal/mole·°C, for H_2O (g) 7 cal/mole·°C, and for CO_2 (g) 7 cal/mole·°C. The peak pressure attained in the explosion is found to be 9.5 atm.

(a) Calculate ΔH_{298} for the combustion of CH_4 according to the reaction

$$CH_4 \text{ (g)} + 2O_2 \text{ (g)} = 2H_2O \text{ (g)} + CO_2 \text{ (g)}.$$

(b) How large is the difference of ΔH and ΔE for this reaction?

(c) Though bombs of adequate strength and pressure gages of adequate range are available, I might still think to get a more accurate value for the heat of combustion by running the reaction as above, with air, rather than with pure oxygen. Why?

9. While doing work against a constant external pressure of 2 atm, one mole of an ideal gas expands from 5 to 15 liters at a constant temperature of 300°K.

(a) For the change produced in the gas by the expansion, what is the value of ΔE? of ΔH?

(b) Calculate the work done and the heat absorbed by the gas during the expansion.

(c) Comment on the possibility of basing on this expansion an engine for high-efficiency continuous conversion of heat into work.

10. Consider the reversible *adiabatic* expansion of an ideal gas. (a) The work done in the expansion is $w = -nC_V(T_2 - T_1)$ for a gas of constant heat capacity. Show that this equation, taken together with the ideal gas law, $PV = nRT$, at once gives the following expression for the work done during the expansion:

$$w = \frac{P_1V_1 - P_2V_2}{\gamma - 1}.$$

(b) Setting out from the perfect gas law and either equation (17) or equation (18), derive, as a third relation obtaining in the adiabatic expansion of an ideal gas, the following:

$$\frac{P_1}{T_1{}^{C_P/R}} = \frac{P_2}{T_2{}^{C_P/R}}.$$

11. The following are three examples of the usefulness of the relation stated in part (b) of the preceding problem:

(a) A fire syringe is a dead-end cylinder with a tightly fitting piston to the inner face of which is attached a bit of tinder. Using a syringe of 1 in^2 cross section, a 147-lb man applies all his weight to the compression of air originally at a temperature of 300°K and a pressure of 1 atm (i.e., 14.7 lb/in^2). Assuming the compression reversible and adiabatic, and assuming further that air is an ideal gas with $C_P = \frac{7}{2}R$, determine the maximum kindling temperature of tinder that must ignite by the end of the compression stroke.

If you know anything of the distinctive feature of the diesel engine, indicate the relevance of this kind of computation to the design of diesel engines.

(b) Liquid air boils at $\sim -190°C$. Assume air to be an ideal gas with $C_P = \frac{7}{2}R$. What must be the pressure of air at 0°C if its reversible adiabatic expansion to a final pressure of 1 atm is barely to cool it to its boiling point?

Air is a *non*ideal gas, between the molecules of which there are small but finite attractive forces. Will this nonideality make the actual cooling greater or less than that calculated above?

(c) In the expansion nozzle of a jet engine thrust is generated by a change reasonably well approximated as the reversible adiabatic expansion of an ideal gas. Assume that the nozzle is fed from a combustion chamber producing gas (with molecular weight 18 and $C_P = \frac{9}{2}R$) at a temperature of 2000°K and a pressure of 30 atm, and that at its exit end the nozzle delivers gas effectively at 1 atm pressure. Calculate (i) the temperature of the exit gas, and (ii) the velocity to which it has been accelerated.

12. (a) In generalizing the Carnot cycle to all materials, we tacitly assumed that, for any given material, two adiabatic lines never intersect. Demonstrate the validity of this assumption by showing that its falsity would make possible a cyclic change with the 100% conversion of heat into work that we never observe in such a change.

(b) Into a small closed room is brought a brand new electric refrigerator, which is then plugged in with its door wide open. What happens to the temperature of the room?

(c) An ice cube weighs about 36 gm (= 2 moles of water). In making one ice cube at 0°C from water at 0°C, how many kilowatt-hours of energy will be used by an ideal Carnot refrigerator, standing in a room at 20°C, if for the conversion of water to ice $\Delta H = -1440 \text{ cal/mole}$ at 0°C, and 1 kwh $= 3.6 \times 10^6$ joules?

13. (a) In an isothermal expansion conducted reversibly, one mole of ideal gas passes from a volume of 1 liter to a volume of 10 liters. Calculate the change of entropy of (i) the system, and (ii) its surroundings.

(b) Consider the same isothermal expansion taking place irreversibly, with the gas expanding into an evacuated region until it reaches its final volume of 10 liters. Calculate the change of entropy of (i) the system, and (ii) its surroundings.

(c) One mole of ideal gas is compressed reversibly and isothermally from a volume of 10 liters to a volume of 1 liter. Calculate the change of entropy of (i) the system, and (ii) its surroundings.

(d) Compare over-all net ΔS produced by (i) the combination of expansion (a) and compression (c) with that produced by (ii) the combination of expansion (b) and compression (c).

14. (a) A closed cylinder is fitted with three diaphragms, as shown in the accompanying figure.

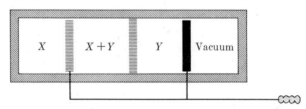

The cylinder is divided in half by a fixed diaphragm selectively permeable to gas Y; the other two diaphragms, of which the one on the left is selectively permeable to gas X and the one on the right is totally impermeable, move together as a linked unit. How much work and heat will be involved in the (i) mixing and (ii) separation of ideal gases that this device makes it possible to conduct reversibly?

(b) A gas X exerts a pressure P_X in some particular volume V; at the same temperature another gas Y exerts a pressure P_Y in *another* numerically equal volume V. The two gases are brought together isothermally so that they occupy the *same* volume V and exert a total pressure $(P_X + P_Y)$. What is the value of ΔS for this change, and how is it reconciled with the randomization that apparently occurs when the gases are mixed?

(c) Assuming all gases ideal, calculate the work invested, the heat dissipated, and the change of entropy when 100 liters of air at 1 atm pressure and 298°K are separated into 79 liters of nitrogen and 21 liters of oxygen measured at 1 atm pressure and 298°K.

15. When a rubber band is stretched no chemical bonds are broken, or even significantly strained, and, to a good first approximation, for the isothermal stretching of rubber $\Delta E = 0$. However, the long polymeric molecules which fall in random coils in unstretched rubber are, by stretching, drawn into a more highly ordered, nearly parallel array of nearly linear molecules. Making constant reference to the cognate case of isothermal expansion and compression of an ideal gas, analyze the changes in entropy and the capacity to deliver work, as well as the transfers of work and heat, to be expected in the reversible and irreversible stretching and relaxation of rubber.

16. (a) A uniform bar containing two moles of metal is so treated that one half is heated to a uniform high temperature T_2 while the other is cooled to a uniform low temperature T_1. The bar is suddenly removed to an insulated enclosure in which—the value of C_P being constant over the range T_1 to T_2—it attains a final temperature of $(T_1 + T_2)/2$. Show that the change of entropy attending this equalization of temperatures is given by the relation

$$\Delta S = C_P \ln \frac{(T_2 + T_1)^2}{4 T_1 T_2}.$$

(b) Showing that in the last formula we will always be taking the logarithm of a number greater than 1, demonstrate that the equalization of temperatures always proceeds with $\Delta S > 0$, i.e., as a spontaneous process.

17. At 0°C the heat of fusion of ice is 1440 cal/mole and the C_P values are 18 cal/mole·°C for water and 9 cal/mole·°C for ice.

(a) One mole of water, set out on a cold night, supercools to the air temperature of −10°C. By analyzing a series of steps through which the end result is attained reversibly, calculate the entropy change of the system when the water at −10°C freezes to ice at the same temperature.

(b) How do you account for the negative value of the entropy change calculate in part (a) for what is obviously a spontaneous process? Calculate the net over-all entropy increase for the process.

18. At its normal boiling point of 373°K water has a heat of vaporization of 545 cal/gm. Taking 18 as the molecular weight of water and assuming that the volume of the liquid is far less than that of the vapor, which may be treated as an ideal gas, calculate the values of q, w, ΔH, ΔE, ΔS, ΔA, and ΔF for the reversible vaporization of 1 mole of water at 373°K.

19. (a) Solid benzene has a vapor pressure of 1.0 mm at −38.5°C and 24.5 mm at 0°C; liquid benzene has a vapor pressure of 26.7 mm at 0°C and 100 mm at 26.1°C. By suitable graphical treatment of these data determine (i) the heat of vaporization of liquid benzene, (ii) the heat of sublimation of solid benzene, (iii) the heat of fusion of benzene, and (iv) the melting point of benzene.

(b) Moderate increases in applied pressure increase the melting point of benzene by 0.03°C/atm. Given that at the melting point the molar volumes of solid and liquid benzene are respectively 76.5 cm³/mole and 87.6 cm³/mole, and using the melting point calculated in (a), determine the heat of fusion of benzene.

(c) Considering the data and the methods involved, how do you appraise the agreement of the results obtained in part (b) and (iii) of part (a)?

20 (a) The melting point of ice is depressed by 0.0075°C/atm imposed pressure. Under 1 atm pressure (ordinarily of air) ice melts at 0°C. At what temperature will ice melt in an evacuated chamber where the only pressure is that of its own vapor (<5 mm mercury at 0°C)?

(b) Water has a heat of vaporization of 9.7 kcal/mole near its normal boiling point of 100°C. At what temperature will water boil atop Pike's Peak under the pressure of ∼0.6 atm there prevailing at 14,100 ft?

(c) Show that for any liquid obeying Trouton's rule the variation of vapor pressure with temperature is given by the relation

$$\ln P = 10.5 \left(1 - \frac{T_B}{T} \right),$$

where T_B is its normal boiling point and P its vapor pressure, in atmospheres, at temperature T.

(d) The relation derived in (c) facilitates rapid order-of-magnitude estimates. Appraise its reliability in the following two calculations. (i) At what temperature can cymene, with $T_B = 177°C$, be vacuum distilled at a pressure of 10 mm mercury? The temperature actually measured is 57°C. (ii) Mercury, with $T_B = 357°C$, should exert what vapor pressure at 18°C? The pressure actually measured is 0.001 mm mercury.

21. (a) A 1% solution (amalgam) of zinc in mercury boils at 358.3°C. The heat of vaporization of mercury is 70.6 cal/gm and the boiling point of pure mercury is 356.58°C. Calculate the boiling point elevation constant for mercury and, taking the atomic weight of zinc as 65.4, determine the state of zinc dissolved in mercury.

(b) From the slope of the line that most nearly approaches the theoretical line in Fig. 26, calculate the heat of fusion of naphthalene. Compare your result with that given in Table 5.

(c) The human red blood cell shrinks when placed in aqueous salt solution more concentrated than 0.9% NaCl and swells in a less concentrated solution. Taking 58.5 as the formula weight of NaCl (assumed 100% ionized) calculate the osmotic pressure of the solution inside the cell, at the normal body temperature of 37°C.

22. (a) From the experimental results plotted in Fig. 28, calculate (with due attention to units) the values of ΔF, ΔH, and ΔS for the following reaction at 150°C: $(CH_3COOH)_2$ (g) $= 2CH_3COOH$ (g).

(b) Consider the following data for the standard states of the indicated materials at 298°K:

	NH_4NO_3 (s)	H_2O (g)
ΔH_f^0 (kcal/mole)	-87.3	-57.8
ΔF_f^0 (kcal/mole)	-45.1	-54.6

Once one envisions the possibility of the reaction

$$NH_4NO_3 \text{ (s)} = N_2 \text{ (g)} + \tfrac{1}{2}O_2 \text{ (g)} + 2H_2O \text{ (g)},$$

the above data are, to the initiate, another way of spelling DANGER. Explain!

23. (a) Derive the Nernst equation by the method indicated in the footnote on p. 80.

(b) The Daniell cell involves the reaction

$$Zn \text{ (s)} + Cu^{++} \text{ (aq)} = Zn^{++} \text{ (aq)} + Cu \text{ (s)}.$$

For this cell at 273°K $\mathfrak{E} = 1.093$ volts and has a temperature coefficient of -4.53×10^{-4} volt/°K. For the above reaction the value of ΔH determined by direct calorimetry is -55.2 kcal; calculate a value of ΔH from the electrochemical data.

24. With reference to the reaction

$$CaCO_3 \text{ (s)} = CaO \text{ (s)} + CO_2 \text{ (g)},$$

consider the following data for the standard states of the indicated materials at 298°K:

	$CaCO_3$ (s)	CaO (s)	CO_2 (g)
ΔH_f^0 (kcal/mole)	-288.5	-151.9	-94.05
S_{298}^0 (cal/mole·°K)	22.2	9.5	51.06

(a) Determine the equilibrium constant for the reaction at 298°K, and state its units.

(b) On the (good) assumption that ΔH for the reaction is substantially constant over the temperature range concerned, calculate the temperature at which the equilibrium pressure of CO_2 becomes equal to 1 atm.

25. The Deacon process, once used for the manufacture of Cl_2 from by-product HCl, depends on a reaction that does not proceed at a detectable rate at low temperatures and that has an unfavorable equilibrium at high temperatures. The reaction is this: $4HCl$ (g) $+ O_2$ (g) $= 2H_2O$ (g) $+ 2Cl_2$ (g). The optimum operating temperature is said to be 470°C. Calculate the equilibrium constant for the reaction at that temperature, given the following data for the standard states of the indicated materials at 298°K:

	HCl (g)	O_2 (g)	H_2O (g)	Cl_2 (g)
ΔH_f^0 (kcal/mole)	−22.1	—	−57.8	—
S_{298}^0 (cal/mole·°K)	44.6	49.0	45.1	53.3

Appendix III
Thermochemical Data at 298.16°K*

Values are given for ΔH_f^0, the standard enthalpy of formation; ΔF_f^0, the standard free energy of formation; S^0, the "absolute" (third principle) entropy; and C_P, the heat capacity at constant pressure—in each case for one mole of material in the indicated state at 1 atm pressure and 25°C. The symbol (aq) refers to a hypothetical ideal aqueous solution in which, at unit molality, the indicated ion has the molal enthalpy and heat capacity one finds for it by extrapolating to infinite dilution. The values for the corresponding ideal salt solutions of unit molality are obtained simply by making the appropriate sums of the values for the component ions. The listed values for ions are based on the convention that takes the value of all the listed properties to be 0.0 for H^+ (aq).

Substance	ΔH_f^0	ΔF_f^0	S^0	C_P
Ag (s)	0.00	0.00	10.206	6.092
AgBr (s)	−23.78	−22.930	25.60	12.52
AgCl (s)	−30.362	−26.224	22.97	12.14
AgI (s)	−14.91	−15.85	27.3	13.01
Al (s)	0.00	0.00	6.769	5.817
Al₂O₃ (s)	−399.09	−376.77	12.186	18.88
Br (g)	26.71	19.69	41.8052	4.9680
Br⁻ (aq)	−28.90	−24.574	19.29	−30.7
Br₂ (g)	7.34	0.751	58.639	8.60
Br₂ (l)	0.00	0.00	36.4	
C (g)	171.698	160.845	37.7611	4.9803
C (diamond)	0.4532	0.6850	0.5829	1.449
C (graphite)	0.00	0.00	1.3609	2.066
CCl₄ (g)	−25.5	−15.3	73.95	19.96
CH₄ (g)	−17.889	−12.140	44.50	8.536
CO (g)	−26.4157	−32.8079	47.301	6.965
CO₂ (g)	−94.0518	−94.2598	51.061	8.874
C₂H₂ (g)	54.194	50.000	47.997	10.499
C₂H₄ (g)	12.496	16.282	52.45	10.41
C₂H₆ (g)	−20.236	−7.860	54.85	12.585

(Continued)

*From *Selected Values of Chemical Thermodynamic Properties*, ed. F.A.Rossini, et. al., National Bureau of Standards Circular 500.

Substance	ΔH_f^0	ΔF_f^0	S^0	C_P
Ca (s)	0.00	0.00	9.95	6.28
Ca^{++} (aq)	−129.77	−132.18	−13.2	
CaCO$_3$ (calcite)	−288.45	−269.78	22.2	19.57
CaCO$_3$ (aragonite)	−288.49	−269.53	21.2	19.42
CaC$_2$ (s)	−15.0	−16.2	16.8	14.90
CaCl$_2$ (s)	−190.0	−179.3	27.2	17.36
CaO (s)	−151.9	−144.4	9.5	10.23
Ca(OH)$_2$ (s)	−235.80	−214.33	18.2	20.2
Cl (g)	29.012	25.192	39.4569	5.2203
Cl$^-$ (aq)	−40.023	−31.350	13.17	−30.0
Cl$_2$ (g)	0.00	0.00	53.286	8.11
Cu (s)	0.00	0.00	7.96	5.848
CuCl (s)	−32.2	−28.4	21.9	
CuCl$_2$ (s)	−49.2			
CuO (s)	−37.1	−30.4	10.4	10.6
Cu$_2$O (s)	−39.84	−34.98	24.1	16.7
Fe (s)	0.00	0.00	6.49	6.03
Fe$_2$O$_3$ (s)	−196.5	−177.1	21.5	25.0
Fe$_3$O$_4$ (s)	−267.0	−242.4	35.0	
H (g)	52.089	48.575	27.3927	4.9680
H$^+$ (g)	367.088			
H$^+$ (aq)	0.00	0.00	0.00	0.00
HBr (g)	−8.66	−12.72	47.437	6.96
HCl (g)	−22.063	−22.769	44.617	6.96
HI (g)	6.20	0.31	49.314	6.97
H$_2$ (g)	0.00	0.00	31.211	6.892
H$_2$O (g)	−57.7979	−54.6357	45.106	8.025
H$_2$O (l)	−68.3174	−56.6902	16.716	17.996
H$_2$S (g)	−4.815	−7.892	49.15	8.12
Hg (g)	14.54	7.59	41.80	4.968
Hg (l)	0.00	0.00	18.5	6.65
HgCl$_2$ (s)	−55.0			18.3
HgO (s, red)	−21.68	−13.990	17.2	10.93
HgO (s, yellow)	−21.56	−13.959	17.5	
Hg$_2$Cl$_2$ (s)	−63.32	−50.350	46.8	24.3
I (g)	25.482	16.766	43.1841	4.9680
I$^-$ (aq)	−13.37	−12.35	26.14	−31.0
I$_2$ (g)	14.876	4.63	62.280	8.81
I$_2$ (s)	0.00	0.00	27.9	13.14

(Continued)

Substance	ΔH_f^0	ΔF_f^0	S^0	C_P
K (s)	0.00	0.00	15.2	6.97
K$^+$ (aq)	−60.04	−67.466	24.5	
KBr (s)	−93.73	−90.63	23.05	12.82
KCl (s)	−104.175	−97.592	19.76	12.31
KI (s)	−78.31	−77.03	24.94	13.16
Mg (s)	0.00	0.00	7.77	5.71
Mg^{++} (aq)	−110.41	−108.99	−28.2	
MgCl$_2$ (s)	−153.40	−141.57	21.4	17.04
MgO (s)	−143.84	−136.13	6.4	8.94
Mg(OH)$_2$ (s)	−221.00	−199.27	15.09	18.41
N (g)	85.565	81.471	36.6147	4.9680
NH$_3$ (g)	−11.04	−3.976	46.01	8.523
NH$_4^+$ (aq)	−31.74	−19.00	26.97	
NO (g)	21.600	20.719	50.339	7.137
NO$_2$ (g)	8.091	12.390	57.47	9.06
N$_2$ (g)	0.00	0.00	45.767	6.960
N$_2$O (g)	19.49	24.76	52.58	9.251
N$_2$O$_4$ (g)	2.309	23.491	72.73	18.90
Na (s)	0.00	0.00	12.2	6.79
Na$^+$ (aq)	−57.279	−62.589	14.4	
NaBr (s)	−86.030			12.5
NaCl (s)	−98.232	−91.785	17.30	11.88
NaHCO$_3$ (s)	−226.5	−203.6	24.4	20.94
NaOH (s)	−101.99			19.2
Na$_2$CO$_3$ (s)	−270.3	−250.4	32.5	26.41
O (g)	59.159	54.994	38.4689	5.2364
OH$^-$ (aq)	−54.957	−37.595	−2.519	−32.0
O$_2$ (g)	0.00	0.00	49.003	7.017
Pb (s)	0.00	0.00	15.51	6.41
PbCl$_2$ (s)	−85.85	−75.04	32.6	18.4
PbO (s, yellow)	−52.07	−45.05	16.6	11.60
PbO$_2$ (s)	−66.12	−52.34	18.3	15.4
Pb$_3$O$_4$ (s)	−175.6	−147.6	50.5	35.14
S (s, rhombic)	0.00	0.00	7.62	5.40
S (s, monoclinic)	0.071	0.023	7.78	5.65
SO$_2$ (g)	−70.96	−71.79	59.40	9.51
SO$_3$ (g)	−94.45	−88.52	61.24	12.10
S$_8$ (g)	24.1			

(Continued)

Substance	ΔH_f^0	ΔF_f^0	S^0	C_P
Si (s)	0.00	0.00	4.47	4.75
SiO$_2$ (s, quartz)	−205.4	−192.4	10.00	10.62
Zn (s)	0.00	0.00	9.95	5.99
ZnCl$_2$ (s)	−99.40	−88.255	25.9	18.3
ZnO (s)	−83.17	−76.05	10.5	9.62